The

Accommodation Guide

1998/9

Use this guide with the official route map
available from Sustrans 0117 929 0888

Gina Farncombe

Curlew Press

5th Edition   *C2C National Cycle Route*

Edited by   Gina Farncombe

Published by   Curlew Press
                     Croft House
                     Newton Reigny
                     Penrith
                     Cumbria CA11 0AY
                     Tel 01768 863298

e-mail   curlew@croftcot.u-net.com
Web page   cumbria.com.accom/cycling.htm

                     © Curlew Press 1998
                     ISBN1 901224 01 5

Distributed by   Cordee Books and Maps
                     3a de Montfort Street
                     Leicester LE1 7HD
                     Tel 0116 254 3579

Contents

Introduction 4
How to start 5
Route map 6-7
Topographical maps 8-10
Accommodation 11-75
Caravan/camping sites 76-77
Youth hostels 77-78
Camping barns 79
Tourist information 80
Bus & train information 80
Weather news 80
Bike repairs & shops 81
Cyclist's check list 82
Advertisements 83-105
How to get home 147
Comments please 106

Accommodation place names (west-east)

Whitehaven 11-15
Workington 16-18
Ennerdale 19
Loweswater 19
Lorton 20
Cockermouth 21-23
Bassenthwaite Lake 23
Newlands Valley 24
Thornthwaite 24
Keswick 25-29
Threlkeld 30
Mungrisdale 30

Troutbeck 31
Berrier 31
Greystoke 32
Motherby 33
Blencowe 33
Newton Reigny 34
Penrith 35-39
Edenhall 40
Langwathby 41
Little Salkeld 42
Winskill 42
Renwick 43
Melmerby 44
Alston 45-50
Leadgate 50
Garrigill 51-53
Nenthead 54-57
Allenheads 58-60
Blanchland 60
Rookhope 61-64
Stanhope 65-66
Consett 67-68
Castleside 68
Stanley 69-70
Beamish 71
Rowlands Gill 71
Chester-le-Street 72-73
Sunderland 74-75
Whitley Bay 114
Tynemouth 112
Newcastle 112
REIVERS ROUTE 107

INTRODUCTION

Welcome to the C2C B&B Guide. This guide is designed to be used with the C2C Sustrans Map obtainable from Sustrans, 35 King Street, Bristol BS1 4DZ, tel. 0117 926 8893.

Your hosts have all been chosen for their understanding of the cyclist's needs, a warm welcome, acceptance of muddy legs, a secure place for your bike and provision of a meal either with them or at a nearby pub. Have a great holiday!

Accommodation is listed from the West to East Coast, not only because the map works this way but also because cyclists benefit from the prevailing wind at their back. If at all possible, please book accommodation, meals and packed lunches in advance, and do not arrive unannounced expecting beds and meals to be available! If you have to cancel a booking, please give the proprietor as much notice as you can so that the accommodation can be re-let.

Your deposit may be forfeited: this is at the discretion of the proprietor.

Suggestions for additional addresses are most welcome, together with your comments.

Please note: the information given in the Guide was correct at the time of printing and was as supplied by the proprietors. No responsibility can be accepted by the Independent B&B Guide as to completeness or accuracy, nor for any loss arising as a result. It is advisable to check the relevant details when booking.

Where do I start the C2C ....?

The best way to cycle the C2C is from West to East coast. If you want to return to the West Coast via the Reivers Route the gradients will be to your advantage.

By Train
To get to Whitehaven or Workington by train you must change on to a local line at CARLISLE. The journey takes about 1 hour,. It follows the coastline and is dramatic and spectacular. Remember, it is essential to book your bike on the train well in advance.

Train enquiries   0345 484 950
Cycle reservations   0345 125 625

Return by Train
From Sunderland, continue to cycle up the coast to the main-line station at Newcastle. Remember, the local train from Sunderland will only take a total of 2 bikes. You will need to make speccial arrangements for more bikes.

By Car
If you have to come by car most landladies will allow you to leave your vehicle with them. There is secure long-term car parking in Whitehaven 'phone the TIC on 01946 852939, or use one of the taxi services on page 00 or cyle back on the Reivers Route!

Note Back-up vehicles are strongly advised to use main roads in order to keep the C2C as traffic free as possible.

C - 2 - C CYCLE ROUTE - WESTERN HALF

N ←

PENNINES

ALSTON
Leadgate
Garrigill
Renwick
Gamblesby
Melmerby
Winskill
Langwathby
Edenhall
Little Salkeld
PENRITH
Motherby
Penruddock
M6

Newton Reigny
Blencow
Greystoke
Berrier
Hutton
Troutbeck
Ullswater
Mungrisdale
Dockray
St. John's in-the-Vale
Thirlmere
KESWICK
Threlkeld
Derwentwater
Bassenthwaite Lake
COCKERMOUTH
Thornthwaite
Braithwaite
Crummock Water
Seaton
Lorton
WORKINGTON
Loweswater
Enmerdale Bridge
WHITEHAVEN
Cleator Moor

CARLISLE
M6

0   10   20
km

6

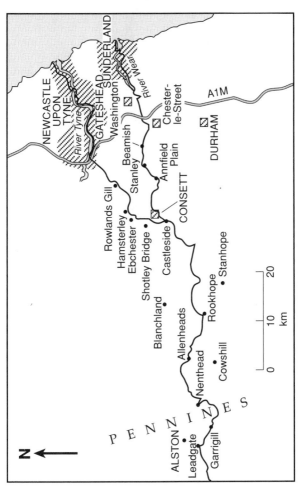

C - 2 - C CYCLE ROUTE - EASTERN HALF

7

TOPOGRAPHICAL CROSS-SECTIONS OF THE C-2-C CYCLE ROUTE

The C-2-C is 140 miles in length. It is strongly advised to ride the route from West to East, giving the benefit of the prevailing westerly winds at your back. As seen from the topographical sections, the uphill biking is long and sharp, and the downhill biking is short and gentle.

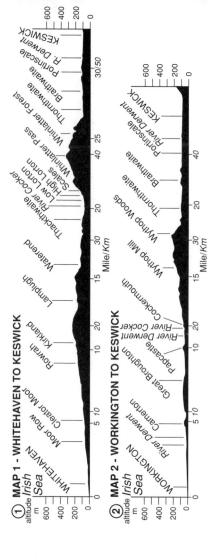

MAP 1 - WHITEHAVEN TO KESWICK

MAP 2 - WORKINGTON TO KESWICK

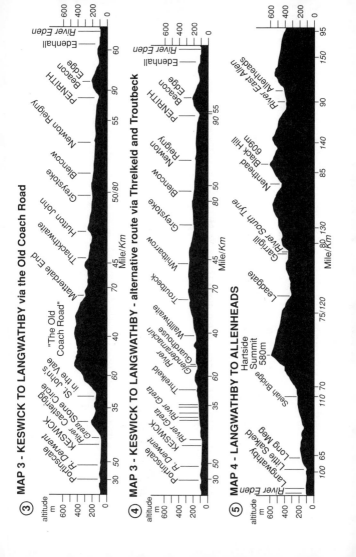

③ MAP 3 - KESWICK TO LANGWATHBY via the Old Coach Road

④ MAP 3 - KESWICK TO LANGWATHBY - alternative route via Threlkeld and Troutbeck

⑤ MAP 4 - LANGWATHBY TO ALLENHEADS

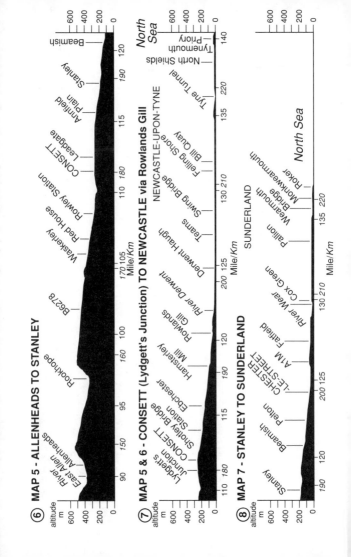

⑥ MAP 5 - ALLENHEADS TO STANLEY

⑦ MAP 5 & 6 - CONSETT (Lydgett's Junction) TO NEWCASTLE via Rowlands Gill

⑧ MAP 7 - STANLEY TO SUNDERLAND

WHITEHAVEN

Whitehaven bay

The town reached its peak of prosperity in the 1740s and 50s with outward trade of coal to Dublin and imports of tobacco from America and rum and sugar from the West Indies. There were early connections with the slave trade together with people settling in America. It was the third busiest port after London and Bristol. The Lowther family laid out the grid pattern for the

Georgian town in the late 1690s. Whitehaven`s most notable scientist was William Brownrigg who studied the explosive mine-gas "fire damp". George Washington's grandmother, Mildred Warner Gale, lived in Whitehaven. Don't forget to dip your bike wheel in the Irish Sea! There is a convenient slipway on the harbour front.

The Beacon Visitor Centre

Whitehaven Tourist Information

PLACES OF INTEREST

Michael Moon's, Roper Street — Bookshop & Gallery: largest bookshop in Cumbria, "vast and gloriously eccentric!"

The Beacon — Local maritime and industrial history within the Harbour Gallery

EATING OUT

Bruno's Restaurant Church St: lively Italian Restaurant 01946 65270

St Nicholas Centre St Nicholas Gardens, Lowther St 01946 64404

The New Expresso 22 Market Place: will do sandwiches to order. Please phone 01946 591548

CYCLE SHOPS

Kershaw's Cycles 125 Queen Street 01946 590700

Mark Taylor Cycles 5/6 New Street 01946 692252

C2C Route Features: *as you leave Whitehaven you will join the Whitehaven-Rowrah cycle path which links the sea to the fells. The railway line was built in the 1850s to carry limestone, coal and iron; it is now a sculpture trail interpreting the geology and industrial history of the region. Further down the C2C the route takes you past the* **Whinlatter Visitor Centre**, *between Lorton and Braithwaite. Here you are in the midst of England's only mountain forest. It contains a wealth of forest habitat information and is well worth a visit if time and energy allow. They have a good tea room too.*

Whitehaven

Mrs B. Barwise   Bell House Farm, St. Bees Road,
                      Whitehaven, Cumbria CA28 9UE
Telephone   **01946 692584**
Rooms   2 single + 2 double
B&B   £16.00-£19.00
Packed lunch   £3.50
Distance from C2C   On route   Pub nearby
"Newly converted self-contained accommodation on a working family farm. Panoramic views, long-stay parking available. A warm welcome awaits you."

Joyce Bailey   The Cross Georgian Guest House,
                      Hensingham, Whitehaven, CA28 8JQ
Telephone   **01946 63716**
Rooms   2 double + 2 single
B&B   £15.00-£20.00
Packed lunch   £2.00-£3.00
Distance from C2C   On route   Pub nearby
"A family-run guest-house on the outskirts of Whitehaven. En-suite rooms with Sky TV. Long-term spacious parking is available by arrangement. Lockable storage for bikes."

Mrs Armstrong   Glen Ard Guest House,
                      Whitehaven, Cumbria CA28 7TY
Telephone   **01946 692249**
Rooms   2 single + 2 double + 2 twin
B&B   £14.00
Evening meal   £5.00   Packed lunch £3.50
Distance from C2C   ¼ mile   Pub nearby
" A family-run guest-house with a private car park only ¼ mile from the C2C route. Early breakfast available if requested."

Whitehaven

Mrs C. M. Oliver Glenlea House, Glenlea Hill, Lowca, Whitehaven, Cumbria CA28 6PS
Telephone **01946 693873** Fax 01946 694350
Rooms 4 single + 8 double
B&B £17.50-£25.00
Evening meal £8.50-£10.50 Packed lunch £3.50
Distance from C2C On route Pub nearby
Family-run guest-house. Private car park. Early breakfast available for those wishing to make the most of the day."
(See advertisement on page 86.)

Mrs Christine Buchanan The Old Granary, Spout House, Sandwith, Whitehaven, CA28 9UG
Telephone **01946 62097**
Rooms 1 twin + 1 double
B&B £16.00 Packed lunch £3.00
Distance from C2C 2 miles Pubs nearby
"Spout House is a barn conversion in a village near to the C2C, with en-suite rooms and tea/coffee-making facilities. A rural start to your journey."

T. Todd The Mansion, Old Woodhouse, Whitehaven, Cumbria CA28 9LN
Telephone **01946 61860** Fax 01946 691270
Rooms 3 double + 1 family
B&B From £11.00
Evening meal £3.00-£6.00
Distance from C2C 600m Pub nearby
"Recently renovated Georgian residence. Sauna, Jacuzzi and sunbed available. Courtesy pick-up if needed, off-street parking. Some en-suite."

Whitehaven

Mrs Janice Telfer Tarn Flatt Hall, Sandwith, Whitehaven,
Cumbria CA28 9UX

Telephone   **01946 692162**
Rooms   2 double
B&B   £16.00
Evening meal   Available   Packed lunch available
Distance from C2C   2 miles   Pub 1 mile

"Quiet, friendly, comfortable B&B on working farm. Good car parking (also long-stay). Whitehaven town centre 4 miles."

Mrs Wright   Tivoli Guest House, 156 Queen Street,
Whitehaven, Cumbria CA28 7BA

Telephone   **01946 67400**
Rooms   3 single + 6 double
B&B   From £14.00
Packed lunch   £3.50
Distance from C2C   On route   Pub nearby

"Homely, offering first-class service and a friendly welcome. Ideally situated in the heart of Whitehaven, 2 minutes from the start of the route."

Waverley Hotel   Tangier Street, Whitehaven, Cumbria
CA28 7UX

Telephone   **01946 694337**   Fax 01946 691577
Rooms   10 single + 10 double
B&B   From £20.00 - £33.00
Evening meal   Available   Packed lunch available
Distance from C2C   ¼ mile   Licensed restaurant

*"300-year-old hotel in centre of historic Whitehaven. All rooms have colour TV and tea/coffee-making facilities. Very near to bus and train station. (**See advertisement on page 85.**)*

WORKINGTON

Helena
Thompson
Museum

Some parts of the town date back to Roman times. Local iron and steel-making helped Workington to expand into a major industrial 18th-century town and port. Famous names linked to the town are Henry Bessemer who introduced his revolutionary steel-making process and Mary Queen of Scots who sheltered in Workington Hall in 1568 on her flight from Scotland. The Hall is now ruined, but is open in summer and is a short distance from the Helena Thompson Museum.

PLACES OF INTEREST

Helena Thompson Museum   Park End Road: a local history gallery together with the famous Clifton dish.

Workington Hall   Apparently haunted by Henry Curwen!

EATING OUT

Impressions   173 Vulcans Lane: Good traditional English food 01900 605446

Super Fish   20 Pow St 01900 604916

CYCLE SHOPS

Traffic Lights Bikes   35 Washington St 01900 603283

New Bike Shop   18-20 Market Place 01900 603337

Workington

Mrs J. Jeffrey   Aykhurst, Hayes Castle Road, Distington,
                       nr Workington, Cumbria CA14 5YB
Telephone   **01946 830372**
Rooms   1 double + 2 twin
B&B   £16.00   Packed lunch £3.00
Distance from C2C   c. 3½ miles   Pub nearby
(No smoking please.) *"Well-appointed, beautifully kept modern bungalow, breakfast served in our conservatory. Convenient for both Workington or Whitehaven C2C start."*

Mrs Alice Clark   The Boston, 1 St Michael's Road,
                       Workington, Cumbria CA14 3EZ
Telephone   **01900 603435**
Rooms   1 family + 2 twin + 1 double/single
B&B   £12.50-£25.00
Distance from C2C   1½ miles   Pub nearby
"A small, homely guest-house with a big reputation. A hearty welcome from a friendly family. First-class English breakfast and good home-cooking. Safe parking for bikes and cars."

Carol Wilson   Green Dragon Hotel, Portland Square,
                       Workington, Cumbria CA14 4BJ
Telephone   **01900 603803**   Fax 01900 872659
Rooms   4 single + 3 double + 3 twin + 1 family
B&B   £15.00-£24.00
Evening meal   £3.95-£11.95 Packed lunch £3.00
Distance from C2C   1mile   Hotel has Public Bar
"11-bedroomed family run hotel set in a Georgian square with modern and comfortable amenities."

Workington

Mrs Caroline Nelson

	Morven House Hotel, Siddick Road, Workington, Cumbria CA14 1LE
Telephone/Fax	**01900 602118**
Rooms	6 twin/double + 2 single
B&B	£19.50-£24.00
Evening meal	£10.00 Packed lunch £4.00
Distance from C2C	On route Pub nearby

ETB 3 Crowns approved. (See advertisement on page 85.)
"A relaxed, informal atmosphere, an ideal stopover for C2C participants near start. Car park and secure cycle storage."

Mrs Hazel Hardy

	Silverdale, 17 Banklands, Workington, Cumbria CA14 3EL
Telephone	**01900 61887**
Rooms	2 double + 2 single
B&B	£13.50-£15.00
Packed lunch	Available on request
Distance from C2C	On route Pub nearby

(No smoking in bedrooms please.) *"Large Victorian house, quiet location, wash-basins in all bedrooms, bathroom has shower, comfy TV lounge, centrally placed, good parking."*

Scotland across the Solway

Ennerdale

Mrs Liz Loxham   Beckfoot, Ennerdale, Cleator CA23 3AU
Telephone   **01946 861235**
Rooms   1 double + 1 twin + 1 double/twin
B&B   £17.50
Evening meal   £10.50   Packed lunch £3.00
Distance from C2C   On route   Pub 2 miles

*"Non-smoking, comfortable and homely accommodation over-
looking Ennerdale Lake. 3-course dinner with coffee, mints,
and a glass of wine. Good breakfast menu."*

Mr Norman   The Shepherds Arms Hotel, Ennerdale
Stanfield   Bridge, Cleator, Cumbria CA23 3AR
Telephone/Fax   **01946 861249**
Rooms   4 double + 3 twin + 1 single
B&B   £26.00
Evening meal   £4.00-£14.50
Distance from C2C   1¼ miles   Hotel has Public Bar

3 Crowns Commended. *"A small friendly hotel in a beautiful
situation, real ale, secure cycle storage, drying facilities, open
all year, all rooms en-suite or with private facilities."*

Loweswater

Mrs Ann Hayton   Brook Farm, Thackthwaite, Loweswater,
                       Cockermouth, Cumbria CA13 0RP
Telephone/Fax   **01900 85606**
Rooms   1 double + 1 family
B&B   From £18.00
Evening meal   £7.00 *(prior notice please)*
Packed lunch   £3.00 *(prior notice please)*
Distance from C2C   On route   Pub 1 mile

(No smoking please.) **1 Crown Commended Tourist Board.**
*"Working farm, quiet, comfortable accommodation, good food,
plenty of hot water, drying facilities, secure garage."*

Lorton

Mrs C. Edmunds   Meadow Bank, High Lorton,
                     Cockermouth, Cumbria CA13 9UG
Telephone/Fax   **01900 85315**
Rooms   2 double + 1 twin
B&B   £16.00-£17.00
Packed lunch   £3.00
Distance from C2C   300 yds   Pub 1 mile
(No smoking please.) *"Comfortable detached house in pictur-
esque village of Lorton, 4 miles from Cockermouth,10 from
Keswick. Excellent , of a very high standard, most welcoming."*

Mrs Armstrong   Terrace Farm, Lorton, Cockermouth,
                     Cumbria CA13 9TX
Telephone   **01900 85278**
Rooms   1 twin/single + 2 double
B&B   £17.00-£18.00
Distance from C2C   c. ½ mile   Pub nearby
1 Crown Commended *"Homely welcome at our family-run
hill-farm set in secluded village location with superb Lakeland
fell views. Good pub food within walking distance."*

Whinlatter Pass

Mrs Ann Roberts   Owl Brook, Whinlatter Pass, Lorton,
                       Cockermouth, Cumbria CA13 9TX
Telephone   **01900 85333**
Rooms   3 double *(singles welcome)*
B&B   £16.50-£17.50
Evening meal   £12.50   Packed lunch £3.25
Distance from C2C   ½ mile   Pub 1¼ miles
(No smoking please.) *"Lakeland green slate bungalow, com-
fortable, central heating, open all year, cycles stored, clothes
dried, OS 163 258."*

COCKERMOUTH

Cockermouth Castle

One of only two "Gem Towns" in the Lake District, Cockermouth is full of fine Georgian architecture and is set on the confluence of two famous salmon rivers: the Derwent and the Cocker. The historic town of Cockermouth has long held an attraction for writers, poets and artists. It is the birthplace of William and Dorothy Wordsworth and has a bustling community air about it. The smell of brewing hops often pervades the air and makes a visit to the pub tempting! The town has had its fair share of troubled times from the Border Raiders and it played host to the fugitive Mary Queen of Scots.

Wordsworth House

Cockermouth

PLACES OF INTEREST

Castlegate House	Frequent exhibitions of interesting contemporary artists 01900 822149
Printing House Museum	'Hands on' experience!

EATING OUT

The Quince & Medlar	13 Castle St: award-winning vegetarian food 01900 823579
Cheers	Main St: Wholesome home-made pasta and pizzas 01900 822109

CYCLE SHOPS

The Wordsworth Hotel Bike Hire	Main St 01900 822757
Derwent Cycles	4 Market Place 01900 822113

C2C Route Features: *take care of the very steep descent through Wythop Woods down to Bassenthwaite lakeside.* ***Thornthwaite Gallery*** *is well worth a visit.*

Miss W. Adams	Castlegate Guest House, 6 Castlegate, Cockermouth, CA13 9EU
Telephone	**01900 826749**
Rooms	4 double + 2 triple + 1 twin
B&B	£17.50 *(single)*-£20.00 *(en-suite)*
Packed lunch	£3.50 *(prior notice please)*
Distance from C2C	On route Pubs nearby

"Grade II-listed Georgian town house in town centre. Indoor lock-up for bikes, friendly atmosphere, spacious accommodation, period furniture. Opposite Quince & Medlar Restaurant."

Cockermouth

John and Susan Graham	Rose Cottage, Lorton Road, Cockermouth, Cumbria CA13 9DX
Telephone/Fax	**01900 822189**
Rooms	6 double + 1 single
B&B	£17.50-£21.00
3-course Dinner	£10.50 Packed lunch £4.25
Distance from C2C	¼ mile Pubs nearby

(No smoking in bedrooms please.) **2 Crowns Commended.**
"Converted 18th-c Inn, family-run, garden, private car park, secure bicycle storage, warm and friendly atmosphere."

Bassenthwaite Lake

Michael and Marilyn Tuppen	Link House, Dubwath, Bassenthwaite Lake, Cockermouth, Cumbria CA13 9YD
Telephone	**017687 76291** Fax 017687 76670
Rooms	2 single + 4 double + 2 twin *(all en-suite)*
B&B	£20.00-£26.00
Evening meal	£13.00
Packed lunch	£3.00 *(prior notice please)*
Distance from C2C	On route Pub nearby

ETB 3 Crowns Commended. *"Link House is a good first stop. Friendly and comfortable, licensed, excellent reputation for imaginative home-cooking and inexpensive wines."*

Thornthwaite

Joy Harrison

	The Swan Hotel, Thornthwaite, Keswick, Cumbria CA12 5SQ
Telephone	**017687 78256**
Rooms	2 single + 7 double + 4 twin
B&B	£20.00-£25.00
Evening meal	Available Packed lunch £3.00
Distance from C2C	On route Hotel has Public Bar

3 Crowns Approved. *"Family-run country Inn. Ideal pre-start and first night. Views of Skiddaw and Bassenthwaite Lake. Secure bike store and workshop, plus bike hire."*

Newlands Valley

Christine Simpson

	Uzzicar Farm, Newlands, Keswick, Cumbria CA12 5TS
Telephone	**017687 78367**
Rooms	2 double + 1 twin
B&B	£14.50-£17.00
Packed lunch	Available on request
Distance from C2C	1 mile Pub ° mile

(No smoking please.) *"A warm welcome awaits you in the peaceful and beautiful Newlands Valley. All bedrooms have wash-basins, central heating, tea/coffee-making facilities."*

KESWICK

Derwentwater

Sandwiched between Derwentwater, Blencathra and Skiddaw, Keswick has a fantastic setting. It became prosperous in the 16th century due to the mining of copper, lead, silver and iron. Mining engineers were imported from Germany: they were treated with suspicion by the locals and forced to make their homes on Derwent Island, but they overcame the hostility as German surnames can still be found amongst the local population. Graphite discovered in Borrowdale in the 1500s gave birth to the famous Cumberland Pencil Company.

The Moot Hall (now the TIC)

Keswick Tourist Information

PLACES OF INTEREST

The Cumberland Pencil Museum	West of town centre 017687 73626
Cars of the Stars	Town centre: vintage cars of famous stars 017687 73757

EATING OUT

Lakeland Pedlar	By central car park: combined tea/bike shop 017687 74492
Maysons	Lake Rd: importers of Eastern goods and excellent food 017687 74104

CYCLE SHOPS

The Stores, Braithwaite	Mr Hindmarch does cycle repairs in the village of Braithwaite 017687 78273
Keswick Mountain Bikes	Behind Pencil Museum: they do hot-air ballooning too! 017687 75202

*C2C Route Features: the route follows the old railway line which crosses and re-crosses the beautiful river Greta. The alternative Old Coach Road route passes **Castlerigg**, a wonderful stone circle.*

Castlerigg Stone Circle

Keswick

Mrs Chris White   Applegarth, Braithwaite, Keswick,
                       Cumbria CA12 5TD
Telephone   **017687 78462**
Rooms   1 single + 2 double
B&B   From £15.00
Packed lunch   From £3.00
Distance from C2C   On route   Pub nearby
"Small friendly B&B. OS 233 243."

Mrs Sharon Helling Beckside Guest House, 5 Wordsworth
                       Street, Keswick, Cumbria CA12 4HU
Telephone   **017687 73093**
Rooms   3 double + 1 twin *(all en-suite)*
B&B   £18.50   Packed lunch £4.00
Distance from C2C   500 yds   Town 3 mins
(No smoking please.) **2 Crowns Commended. RAC and AA
Highly Commended.***"Close to town centre, small, homely,
with tastefully decorated bedrooms. Good hearty breakfasts
for hungry cyclists.1 minute from route."*

S. R. North   Century House, 17 Church Street,
                       Keswick, Cumbria CA12 4DT
Telephone   **017687 72843**
Rooms   3 double + 1 twin + 1 family
B&B   £16.50-£19.50
Packed lunch   £3.00
Distance from C2C   On route   Pub nearby
(No smoking please.) *"Lovely Victorian house offering private
or en-suite facilities, with a warm and friendly welcome."*

Keswick

Sonja Meere Cranford House, 18 Eskin Street, Keswick, Cumbria CA12 4DG

Telephone	**017687 71017** Fax: 017687 72335
Rooms	2 single + 1 double + 1 twin
B&B	£15.00 Packed lunch £2.50
Distance from C2C	On route Pub nearby

(No smoking please.) "Friendly B&B accommodation in residential area, 5 minutes walk from town centre. Lounge with open fire. Drying facilities available."

Bill and Derwentdale Guest House, 8 Blencathra
Elizabeth Riding Street, Keswick, Cumbria CA12 4HP

Telephone	**017687 74187**.
Rooms	3 double + 2 single + 1 twin
B&B	£15.00-£18.00 *(some en-suite)*
Evening meal	£9.50 Packed lunch £3.50
Distance from C2C	On route Pub nearby

(No smoking please.) **Listed Commended.** "Friendly, comfortable, centrally-heated guesthouse. Colour TV, tea/coffee-making facilities, hair dryers, close to town centre."

Red squirrels are a common sight in the woods around Derwentwater

Keswick

Mrs Jackie Robinson

Greystoke House, Leonard Street, Keswick, Cumbria CA12 4EL

Telephone **017687 72603**

Rooms 4 double + 2 single

B&B £16.00-£18.00.

Evening meal £9.50   Packed lunch £3.50

Distance from C2C On route   Pub nearby

ETB 2 Crowns Commended, RAC Acclaimed. *"Quietly situated Lakeland town house. Good food, comfortable accommodation, relaxed atmosphere. Secure yard for cycles."*

Graeme and Gill Winter

Rivendell, 23 Helvellyn Street, Keswick, Cumbria CA12 4EN

Telephone **017687 73822**

Rooms 3 double + 2 twin + 1 family + 1 single

B&B £17.00-£20.00

Evening meal £10.00   Packed lunch £3.00

Distance from C2C On route   Pub nearby

(No smoking please.) "Warm, comfortable accommodation. Hearty brekkies for all you bike trekkies. Secure storage and drying facilities. Launderette and phone just over the road."

A Keswick scene

Threlkeld

Chris and Caroline Briggs

Scales Farm Country Guest House, Scales, Threlkeld, Keswick, CA12 4SY

Telephone/Fax	**017687 79660**
e-mail	scales@scalesfarm.demon.co.uk
Rooms	3 double + 1 family + 1 twin
B&B	From £23.00 Packed lunch £4.00
Distance from C2C	On route Pub nearby

ETB 2 Crown Highly Commended. *"A welcoming traditional fells farmhouse oozing charm and character. Superb views over the rolling Cumbrian fells."*

Mungrisdale

John McKeever

The Mill Inn, Mungrisdale, nr Penrith, Cumbria CA11 0XR

Telephone/Fax	**017687 79632**
e-Mail	the_mill_inn@compuserve.com
Rooms	1 single + 3 double + 5 twin
B&B	£22.50-£28.50
Meals	£4.00-£20.00, served all day
Packed lunch	£2.50-£3.95 Public bar
Distance from C2C	On new amended route

(Smoking in bar only please.) **3 Crown Commended, AA QQQ.** *"Traditional 16th-c Inn. Beautiful location. Log fire, warm welcome. Excellent accommodation, home-made food, and real ales. Lock-ups available. You will want to come back!"*

Swaledales

Troutbeck

Mrs J. Wilson
Gill Head Farm, Troutbeck, nr Penrith, Cumbria, CA11 0ST **017687 79652**

Rooms	3 double + 2 twin *(all en-suite)*
B&B	From £18.00
Evening meal	£7.00 *(prior notice please)*
Packed lunch	£3.00 *(prior notice please)*
Distance from C2C	On route Pub nearby

"Comfortable 17th-c farmhouse, oak beams, log fires, traditional home-cooking, tea/coffee-making facilities, colour TV, central heating, plus a level, sheltered campsite, laundry and shop for campers." **(See advertisement on page 86.)**

Ron and Anne Ross
Greenah Crag Farm, Troutbeck, nr Penrith, Cumbria CA11 0SQ

Telephone/Fax	**017684 83233**
E-mail	greenah.crag@btinternet.com
Rooms	2 double + 1 twin *(en suite available)*
B&B	£16.00-£22.00
Distance from C2C	½ mile Pub nearby

(No smoking please.) "A warm welcome from Ron and Anne Ross at their 17th-c farmhouse, central heating, tea/coffee-making facilities, TV lounge, bike lock-up."

Berrier

Mary Harris
Whitbarrow Farm, Berrier, nr Penrith, Cumbria CA11 0XB

Telephone/Fax	**017684 83366** Mobile 0370 325971
Rooms	2 double en-suite + 1 twin
B&B	£19.00-£23.00
Packed lunch	£3.50 *(prior notice please)*
Distance from C2C	On route Pub nearby

"Dairy farm of 250 acres, set in delightful hilltop position. Warm welcome. Good hearty English breakfast to set you on your way." **(See advertisement on page 88.)**

Greystoke

**Mrs Jean
  Ashburner**
Telephone
Rooms
B&B
Distance from C2C

Lattendales Farm, Berrier Road,
Greystoke, nr Penrith CA11 0UE
017684 83474.
1 double + 2 twin
£15.00-£16.00
On route   Pub nearby

(No smoking please.) "17th-c farmhouse of character with comfortable accommodation. Interesting stone-built village which nestles round the towering walls of Greystoke Castle."

Mrs Ann Cooper

Telephone
Rooms
B&B
Distance from C2C

Meldene, Icold Road, Greystoke,
nr Penrith, Cumbria CA11 0UG
017684 83856
1 double + 1 twin
£15.00-£17.50 Packed lunch £3.00
On route   Pub nearby

(No smoking please.) "Detached family home near village centre. Tea/coffee-making facilities in all rooms. Secure garage for cycles."

Mrs W. Theakston

Telephone/Fax
Rooms

B&B
Distance from C2C

Orchard Cottage, Church Rd, Greystoke,
nr Penrith, Cumbria CA11 0TW
017684 83264
1 double *(private facilities)*
+ 1 family *(en-suite)*
From £18.00 Packed lunch £3.00
On route   Pub nearby

(No smoking please.) "Orchard Cottage offers excellent accommodation with cleanliness, comfort and warmth, and a hearty breakfast. Drying facilities available. On C2C route."

Motherby

Mrs Jackie Freeborn Motherby House, Motherby, nr Penrith, Cumbria CA11 0RS.
Telephone **017684 83368**
Rooms 2 family/twin B&B £15.50
Evening meal £9.00 *(prior notice please)*
Packed lunch £3.50 *(prior notice please)*
Distance from C2C 1 mile Pub less than 1 mile

"An 18th-c house. Warm and friendly, beamed lounge, log fires, drying facilities, safe storage for bikes, and good food. Muddy bikers welcome!" **(See advertisement on page 88.)**

Blencowe

Martin Armstrong The Crown Inn, Blencowe, nr Penrith, Cumbria CA11 0DG
Telephone **017684 83369**
Rooms 2 double + 1 single *(no smoking please)*
B&B £17.00
Evening meal From £4.50 Packed lunch £3.00
Distance from C2C On route

"Friendly cheerful village pub, cosy, good food, real ales: the cyclists choice after a challenging day in the wilds."

Mrs Barbara Fawcett Little Blencowe Farm, Blencowe, nr Penrith, Cumbria CA11 0DG
Telephone/Fax **017684 83338**
Rooms 1 family + 1 double + 1 twin
B&B £15.00-£17.50
Packed lunch £3.00
Distance from C2C On route Pub nearby

(No smoking in bedrooms please.) *"Farmhouse accommodation on working farm, plus small campsite. Driving horses kept for competitions. All rooms can be let as singles."*

33

Newton Reigny

William O'Donovan
Newton Rigg College, nr Penrith, Cumbria CA11 0AH.

Telephone	**01768 863791** Fax 01768 687249
e-mail	resm11@newtonrigg.ac.uk.
Rooms	250 single + 2 double + 26 twin
B&B	£13.00-£19.00
Evening meal	From £3.50 Packed lunch from £2.50
Distance from C2C	On route Pub on site

Approved 1 Crown, Welcome Host. *"On C2C at 55 miles mark. Standard and en-suite rooms; secure cycle sheds; bar; shop; launderette formal gardens; meals available to non-residents. Reservations not always necessary."*

Peter Ingham
The Sun Inn, Newton Reigny, nr Penrith, Cumbria CA11 0AP

Telephone	**01768 867055**
Rooms	2 double + 2 twin + 1 family
B&B	From £20.00
Evening meals	From £5.00 Packed lunch £3.00
Distance from C2C	On route

"Traditional country Inn. Real ales. Log fire. Good pub food and warm atmosphere. Children welcome."

PENRITH

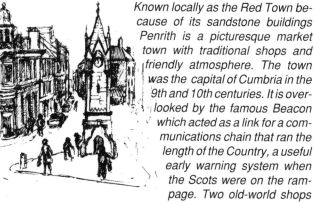

Known locally as the Red Town because of its sandstone buildings Penrith is a picturesque market town with traditional shops and friendly atmosphere. The town was the capital of Cumbria in the 9th and 10th centuries. It is overlooked by the famous Beacon which acted as a link for a communications chain that ran the length of the Country, a useful early warning system when the Scots were on the rampage. Two old-world shops have survived in a time-warp: Grahams, Penrith's answer to Fortnum and Masons, and Arnisons, the drapers, established in 1740 and once the home of Wordworth's grandparents.

Until the end of the 14th-c the town had no water supply. In 1385 Bishop Strickland diverted Thacka Beck from the river Peterill and an environmentally aware agreement allowed the townspeople to draw daily only as much water from the Peterill as would flow through the eye of a millstone.

Penrith Castle dates from 1897 when an existing pele tower was crenellated. The area would certainly have witnessed some violent times from across the Borders in the past.

Penrith Tourist Information

PLACES OF INTEREST

Robinson's School Middlegate: TIC and Museum. Local history on show and regular exhibitions

St Andrew's Church The Giant's Grave in the Churchyard: legendary slayer of monsters from Inglewood Forest!

EATING OUT

The Narrowgate Coffee Shop The Narrows: best coffee in town 01768 862599

The Bewick Princes Street 01768 864764

A Taste of Bengal Stricklandgate 01768 891700

CYCLE SHOPS

Arragons' Brunswick Road 01768 890344

Harpers Cycles 1-2 Middlegate 01768 864475

Saddleback Cycles Cycle Hire **(See page 102)**

*C2C Route Features: the Watermill at Little Salkeld, organic millers with art gallery and café. **Long Meg and her Daughters,** a pre-historic stone circle (don't dance on the Sabbath, you may be turned into one of these stones!). If you go through Melmerby don't miss the famous **Village Bakery**, the **Shepherds Inn** or the **Isis Gallery**.*

Long Meg and her Daughters

Penrith

Mrs Blundell Albany House, 5 Portland Place,
Penrith, Cumbria CA11 7QN
Telephone **01768 863072**
Rooms 1 family (sleeps 5) + 1 double + 3 triple
B&B From £16.50 Packed lunch £3.50
Distance from C2C On route Pub nearby
ETB Commended. AA QQQ. *"Mid-Victorian town house offering spacious comfortable rooms with tea/coffee-making facilities, colour/satellite TV, free clothes drying."*

Mrs P. Allison 7 Alexandra Road, Penrith,
Cumbria CA11 9AL
Telephone **01768 863950**
Rooms 2 double
B&B £13.50
Packed lunch Available on request
Distance from C2C On route Pub nearby
"Corner sandstone house in residential area. Assured of a warm welcome, with a cup of tea and hot shower."

Mrs Carole Tully Brandelhow Guest House, 1 Portland
Place, Penrith, Cumbria CA11 7QW
Telephone **01768 864470**
Rooms 4 double/twin + 1 family
B&B £15.00-£18.00
Packed lunch £3.50 *(prior notice please)*
Distance from C2C On route Pub nearby
1 Crown Commended. *"Victorian town house on C2C route. Comfortable beds and a good English breakfast for the weary cyclist! Tea/coffee-making facilities, colour TV."*

Penrith

Ann Clark

The Friarage, Friargate, Penrith, Cumbria CA11 7XR

Telephone	**01768 863635**
Rooms	2 double + 1 single
B&B	£15.00-£17.00
Packed lunch	Available on request
Distance from C2C	On route Pub nearby

"Historic house. Clean, comfortable, spacious, tea/coffee-making facilities, colour TV, good breakfast, warm welcome. Open Easter to September."

Mr T. Niedt

The George Hotel, Devonshire Street, Penrith, Cumbria CA11 7SU

Telephone	**01768 862696** Fax 01768 868223
Rooms	15 double + 15 single
B&B	£42.75-£58.00
Evening meal	£14.00 Packed lunch £4.50
Distance from C2C	On route Hotel has Public Bar

3 Crowns Commended. *"Old coaching Inn, privately owned in the town centre. All rooms with private bathroom/shower, radio, colour TV, telephone, tea/coffee-making facilities."*

Julie and Mike Davidson

Glendale Guest House, 4 Portland Place, Penrith, Cumbria CA11 7QN

Telephone	**01768 862579**
Rooms	3 family + 1 double + 1 single
B&B	£16.00-£20.00
Packed lunch	£3.00
Distance from C2C	On route Pub nearby

Listed / Commended. *"Spacious town house. Family-run with friendly and comfortable atmosphere, special diets catered for on request. Washing and drying facilities available."*

Penrith

Sylvia Jackson

Norcroft Guest House, Graham St, Penrith, Cumbria CA11 9LQ

Telephone/Fax **01768 862365**

Rooms 3 double + 3 twin + 1 triple + 1 single

B&B £16.00-£21.00

Evening meal £5.95 *(prior notice please)*

Packed lunch £3.50.

Distance from C2C On route Pub nearby

3 Crowns Commended. *"Large Victorian house, comfortable rooms, mostly en-suite, tea/coffee-making facilities, colour TV, drying facilities."*

Mrs D Bardgett

27 Sandgate, Penrith, Cumbria CA11 7TJ

Telephone **01768 865057**

Rooms 1 double + 1 family *(all en-suite)*

B&B £15.00 Packed lunch £3.00

Distance from C2C On route Pub next door

"Right on cycle route, with secure area for cycles."

Mr and Mrs Davies

Woodland House Hotel, Wordsworth Street, Penrith, CA11 7QY

Telephone **01768 864177** Fax 01768 890152

E-mail idaviesa@cix.co.uk.

Rooms 5 double + 3 single *(all en-suite)*

B&B £28.00-£35.00

Evening meal £9.50 *(prior notice please)*

Packed lunch £3.00 *(prior notice please)*

Distance from C2C On route Pub nearby

(No smoking please.) **2 Crowns Commended.** *"Elegant, spacious licensed private hotel at the bottom of Beacon Hill, tea/coffee-making facilities, colour TV. Library of tourist info."*

Edenhall

Richard Burton   The Edenhall Hotel, Edenhall,
                        nr Penrith, Cumbria CA11 8SX
Telephone/Fax   **01768 881454**
Rooms   20 double + 8 single *(all en-suite)*
B&B   £22.50-£35.00
Evening meal   From £5.50   Packed lunch £3.95
Distance from C2C   On route   Hotel has Public Bar

3 Crowns. *"Country house hotel in beautiful surroundings. TV, telephone, and tea/coffee-making facilities in all rooms. Excellent food."*

Mrs Jane Metcalfe   Home Farm, Edenhall, nr Penrith,
                        Cumbria CA11 8SS
Telephone   **01768 881203**
Rooms   1 family + 1 double + 1 twin
B&B   £16.00-£20.00
Distance from C2C   On route   Pub 5 minutes walk

"Home-from-home atmosphere, spacious, attractively furnished rooms and bathroom/ shower room. Visitors lounge, TV and tea/coffee-making facilities." **(See advertisement on page 90.)**

Langwathby

Mrs Karen Peet Hayloft Bunkhouse, Langwathby Hall,
Langwathby, nr Penrith, CA10 1LW
Telephone **01768 881661** Fax 01768 881802
Rooms 36 bunks (2 cubicles of 8 + 2 of 10)
B&B £11.50 (Continental) £13.00 (English)
Packed lunch £3.50
Distance from C2C On route Pub 150 yds
(No smoking please.) *"Very comfortable bunkhouse accommodation in converted stable loft, with hot showers, and breakfast served in the farmhouse. Eden Ostrich World."*

Mrs Lorna Egan Langley House, Langwathby,
nr Penrith, Cumbria CA10 1LW
Telephone/Fax **01768 881571**
Rooms 2 double/twin/family
B&B £19.00 Packed lunch £3.50
Distance from C2C On route Pub nearby
(No smoking please.) **Listed Highly Commended.** *"Weary cyclists will love the warm, spacious, comfortable rooms, plus locked cycle storage, washing/drying service, and generous breakfasts." (See advertisement on page 90.)*

Clive Gravett Langstanes, Culgaith Road,
Langwathby, nr Penrith CA10 1NA
Telephone/Fax **01768 881004**
Rooms 2 double + 1 twin *(most en-suite)*
B&B £16.00-£19.50
Packed lunch From £3.50
Distance from C2C On route Pub 300 yds
"Comfortable sandstone house on route, tea/coffee-making facilities, colour TV, secure bike storage, drying facilities."

Little Salkeld

Anne and Maurice Barnes	Bank House Farm and Stables, Little Salkeld, nr Penrith, Cumbria CA10 1NN
Telephone	**01768 881257**
Rooms	1 double + 1 family + 1 twin + 1 single
B&B	£16.00-£20.00 Packed lunch £3.50
Distance from C2C	On route Pub 1 mile

"Great B&B. Enjoy the company of beautiful resident race-horses in relaxing surroundings. Aga-cooked breakfast with home-made bread! Lifts arranged to pub for the leg weary!) "

Winskill

June H. Toms	The Firs Country Guest House, Winskill, nr Penrith, Cumbria CA10 1PB
Telephone	**01768 881590**
Rooms	1 single + 1 double + 1 twin
B&B	£17.00 Packed lunch £3.50
Distance from C2C	½ mile Pub 3 miles

"A no-smoking establishment with secure parking for cycles. Packed lunches are available if ordered at time of booking, and evening meals are available at local country pubs. Transportation can be provided at £1 per person."

(See advertisement page 94.)

A fellside farm

42

Renwick

Mike and   Howscales, Kirkoswald, nr Penrith,
  Toni Parsons   Cumbria CA10 1JG

Telephone	**01768 898666** Fax 01768 898710
Rooms	1 double + 1 twin (+ extra bed)
B&B	£14.00-£18.00
Evening meal	From £6.00 Packed lunch £3.50
Distance from C2C	¼ mile Pub 1½ miles

(No smoking please.) "Homely comfortable farmhouse ½ mile from C2C before climb up Hartside. Home-cooked meals, afternoon teas, secure lock-up and repair facilities."

Sandy Hawkyard   Horse & Jockey House, Renwick,
                    nr Penrith, Cumbria CA10 1JT

Telephone	**01768 898579**
Rooms	1 family
B&B	From £12.00
Evening meal	£8.00 Packed lunch on request
Distance from C2C	1 mile Pub 2½ miles

"Renwick is a peaceful and unique fellside farming village, 1 mile from the C2C before the big climb up Hartside. Family room. Tame children and friendly dogs welcome."

Pamela Bonnick   Scalehouse Farm , Scalehouses,
                    Renwick, nr Penrith, Cumbria CA10 1JY

Telephone/Fax	**01768 896493**
Rooms	2 double + 1 twin
B&B	£14.00-£17.00
Evening meal	From £7.00 Packed lunch £3.50
Distance from C2C	2 miles Pub 2½ miles

(No smoking please.) "Old farmhouse in unique position before the ascent of Pennines. Alternative breakfast of home-made breads and jams, comfy lounge, TV, books, games."

Melmerby

This delightful village is 3 miles off the route but is well worth the visit as it has so much to offer and lots of facilities.

Thomas and	Bolton Farmhouse, Melmerby,
Margaret Frazer	nr Penrith, Cumbria CA10 1HF
Telephone	**01768 881851**
Rooms	1 single + 1 double + 1 twin
B&B	£15.00
Evening meal	From £5.00 Packed lunch £3.00
Distance from C2C	3 miles Pub 20 metres

"Clean, comfortable and friendly 18th-c village farmhouse, centrally situated, in an 'area of outstanding natural beauty'. All welcome. Worth a visit."

Mrs Edith James	Greenholme, Melmerby, nr Penrith,
	Cumbria CA10 1HB
Telephone	**01768 881436**
Rooms	2 double/twin + 1 double/family en-suite
B&B	From £16.00
Distance from C2C	3 miles Pub nearby

(No smoking please.) "Comfortable accommodation for the weary cyclist. All rooms have tea/coffee-making facilities. A good English breakfast before the big climb up Hartside."

Margaret Morton	Meadow Bank, Melmerby, nr Penrith,
	Cumbria CA10 1HF
Telephone	**01768 881652**
Rooms	2 double + extra bed
B&B	From £15.00
Distance from C2C	3 miles Pub 100 yds

(No smoking please.) "Friendly warm atmosphere. Last stop before the big climb up Hartside. Beautiful views of Pennines from back of house."

ALSTON

Market Square

A picture postcard Cumbrian market town hidden away in England's last wilderness. Cobbled streets wind steeply up to the old market square where you will find quaint old cafés and shops. This historic town, built on the confluence of the South Tyne and the river Nent, owes much to the lead-mining heritage of the area. The mines and their machinery are silent now, but scattered hill farms where mining families grew crops to subsidise their meagre wages and the haunting sound of the curlew still remain. Once you visit this area, its beauty and history will lure you back to explore more of its secrets.

South Tynedale Railway

Alston Tourist Information

PLACES OF INTEREST

Hartside Nursery Garden
On route 1 mile from Alston: rare and unusual alpine plants

South Tynedale Railway
TIC and beautifully restored Victorian station, England's highest narrow-gauge railway 01434 381696

EATING OUT

Gossipgate Gallery
The Butts, back of the old market: tea room and craft gallery 01434 381806

The Angel
Town Centre 01434 381363

C2C Route Features: the route does not officially go through Alston. It goes to Leadgate and thence to Garrigill and Nenthead. Garrigill has a post office and pub. Nenthead has a newly opened **Mines Heritage Centre,** *a pub, a cafè and village shop. If you take the Stanhope route, Killhope Lead-mining Centre is excellent.*

WARNING! *This area is in a very remote corner of the UK: places to buy food or stay overnight are few and far between.*

Alston Moor

Alston

Joe and Sam Pester Albert Guest House, Townhead, Alston, Cumbria CA9 3SL
Telephone **01434 381793** Mobile 0498 565748
Web http://www.cumbria.com/accom/alberthouse.htm
Rooms 3 double/twin B&B £15.00-£17.50
Evening meal £5.00-£10.00 Packed lunch £3.50
Distance from C2C 1½ miles Pub nearby
(No smoking please.) **ETB 1 Crown Commended.** *"Comfortable, fine period house. Warm and friendly service. En-suite. Vast storage area, drying room. Special diets. Cyclists spoilt!"*

Patricia Davidson Alricia, 10 Bruntley Meadows, Alston, Cumbria CA9 3UX
Telephone **01434 381307**
Rooms 3 double or single
B&B £14.00-£17.00
Evening meal £8.00 Packed lunch £3.00
Distance from C2C 1½ miles Pub nearby
(No smoking please.) *"Alricia is a new stone-built bungalow in a quiet scenic part of town. Very clean, comfortable and homely accommodation."*

Blueberry's Blueberry's Guesthouse and Restaurant, Market Pl, Alston CA9 3QN
Telephone **01434 381928**
Rooms 3 double/twin/family
B&B £15.50-£18.00
Evening meal Available Packed lunch available
Distance from C2C Alston town centre Pubs 25 yds
(No smoking in bedrooms please.) **Listed, Commended.** *"Queen Anne Grade II Listed town house, 25 yds from shops and pubs. Full Cumbrian breakfast, under-cover cycle store."*

Alston

Mrs Carolyn Williams

Bridge End Farm, Alston, Cumbria CA9 3BJ   Telephone **01434 381261**

Rooms	2 double + 1 twin + 1 family
B&B	£15.50-£17.50
Evening meal	£9.00 Packed lunch £3.50
Distance from C2C	On route Pub 400 yds

(No smoking please.) "18th-c farmhouse. Home-cooking. Generous breakfast. Clean, comfortable accommodation and a warm welcome awaits."

Mrs Jean Best

Chapel House, Alston, Cumbria CA9 3SH

Telephone	**01434 381112**
Rooms	2 double + 1 single
B&B	£13.00-£15.00
Evening meal	£6.00 *(prior notice please)*
Packed lunch	£2.50
Distance from C2C	c. 2 miles Pub nearby

(No smoking in some areas please.) **Approved. Listed.** "17th-c Chapel, a friendly welcome to clean, comfortable accommodation and good home-cooking."

David Hymers

The Cumberland Hotel, Townfoot, Alston, Cumbria CA9 3HX

Telephone	**01434 381875** Fax 01434 382035
Rooms	3 double + 2 twin + 3 family
B&B	£20.00-£24.00
Evening meal	From £4.00 Packed lunch £3.00
Distance from C2C	On route Hotel has Public Bar

"All rooms en-suite. Lunch and dinner available from a bar or restaurant menu. Bike storage, drying room and cleaning facilities. Small fee for use of nearby indoor swimming pool and sauna." *(See advertisement on page 92.)*

Alston

Mrs Celia Pattison   Highfield, Bruntley Meadows,
Alston, Cumbria CA9 3UX

Telephone	**01434 382182**
Rooms	1 double en-suite + 1 twin + 1 single
B&B	£14.00-£17.00
Evening meal	£7.00 Packed lunch £3.00
Distance from C2C	1½ miles Pub nearby

(No smoking in bedrooms please.) "Modern bungalow with magnificent views of Pennines. Home-baking. TV, tea/coffee-making facilities in all rooms."

Mr and Mrs   Lowbyer Manor Country House Hotel,
P.J. Hughes   Alston, Cumbria CA9 3JX

Telephone	**01434 381230** Fax 01434 382937
Rooms	10 double + 2 single *(all en-suite)*
B&B	£29.50
Dinner (à la carte)	From £16.50 Packed lunch £5.00
Distance from C2C	c. 1 mile Pub nearby

3 Crowns Commended. *"Family-run 17th-c manor, once Jacobite owned, in quiet wooded location on edge of Alston. Secure garage for bikes."*

Mrs Vicky   Nentholme B&B, The Butts, Alston,
Thompson   Cumbria CA9 3JQ

Telephone/Fax	**01434 381523** Mobile 0378 119774
Rooms	5 double/twin + 1 single
B&B	£15.00-£20.00
Evening meal	£11.00 Packed lunch £3.50
Distance from C2C	150 yds Pub nearby

(No smoking please.) **ETB 2 Crowns Commended.** *"In its own grounds offering quiet, clean and comfortable accommodation, and an excellent cycle repair and hire service."*

Alston

Adam Ferguson	St Paul's Mission, Townhead, Alston, Cumbria CA9 3SG
Telephone	**01768 862951**
Rooms	36 bed-cubicled accommodation
B&B	£10.00-£15.00
Distance from C2C	2 miles Pub nearby

(No smoking please.) "100 yds from Market Square, 8 showers and W.C.s, indoor bike security, sauna, large lounge, Sky TV, cooking , washing/drying rooms, full central heating, large garden." *(**Please see advertisement on page 91.**)*

Leadgate

Mike and Clare Le Marie	Brownside House, Leadgate, Alston, Cumbria CA9 3EL
Telephone	**01434 382169** Fax 01434 382100
Rooms	1 family + 1 twin + 1 single
B&B	£15.00
Evening meal	£6.00 Packed lunch £2.50
Distance from C2C	On route Pub 2 miles

"Country situation with superb views. Residents lounge with TV, children welcome. Drying facilities available. Hot bath for cyclists, cold shower for bikes!"

GARRIGILL

This peaceful little village was once a bustling lead mining community. In 1831 the population was 1,614, today it is a mere 225. The rounded hillocks around the village betray the site of lead mine workings, many of them tree covered, but in the mining heyday not a tree was to be seen between Nenthead and Alston.

The surrounding hillsides are a honeycomb of mining tunnels. When times were hard for the miners they would turn their skills to poaching the local game. A pheasant or hare poached from the local gentry was a welcome feast for a hungry mining family. At one time the King's Hussars were called in to restrain the poachers, but the men of Garrigill knew where to hide!

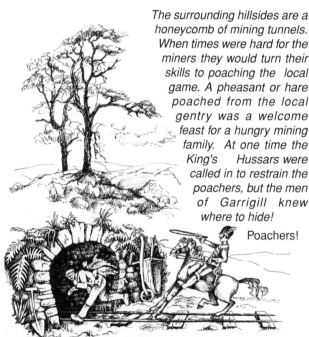

Poachers!

Garrigill has a Pub and a Post Office, and some guesthouses do excellent evening meals.

Garrigill

Mrs Pauline Platts   High Windy Hall Hotel & Restaurant,
(on B6277)   Above Garrigill, Alston, CA9 3EZ
Telephone   **01434 381547**   Fax 01434 382477
E-mail   sales@hwh.u-net.com.
Rooms   2 double+2 twin+1 family *(all en-suite)*
B&B   £25.00-£30.00
Evening meal   £18.00   Packed lunch £3.50
Distance from C2C   200 metres   Pub ½ mile
2 Crowns Highly Commended. *"Family-run licensed hotel, good food, interesting wine list, peaceful views overlooking South Tyne Valley, well-deserved luxury after Hartside Pass."*

Karen Wells   Ivy Farmhouse, Garrigill, CA9 3DU
Telephone/Fax   **01434 382501**
E-mail   100125,2716@compuserve.com.
Rooms   3 double or twin + 2 family
B&B   £15.00-£20.00
Evening meal   From £10.00   Packed lunch£3.00
Distance from C2C   On route   Pub nearby
(No smoking please.) **Listed Commended (AA : QQ)**
"17th-c farmhouse, full of character with spacious en-suite bedrooms, located in village. Cycle storage, residents' lounge, central heating, drying room, great food and friendly hosts."

Lead Mining

Garrigill

Pat Dent   Low Crossgill Farm, Garrigill, Alston,
                          Cumbria CA9 3HE
Telephone   **01434 381383**
Rooms   1 double/twin + 1 family + 1 single
B&B   £16.00-£20.00
Evening meal   £11.00   Packed Lunch £3.50.
Distance from C2C   ¼ mile   Pub nearby
(No smoking please.) **2 Crowns Highly Commended.** *"A working hill farm, furnished to a high standard, centrally-heated, en-suite rooms, all home-cooking, a warm welcome."*

Anne Bramwell   Post Office, Garrigill, Alston,
                          Cumbria CA9 3DS
Telephone   **01434 381257**
Rooms   1 double + 2 twin + 1 single
B&B   £16.00   Packed lunch £3.00
Distance from C2C   On route   Pub nearby
(No smoking please.) "The Post Office is a 300 year old house. Tea/coffee-making facilities, radio alarms and hair dryers in all rooms, separate residents' lounge with TV."

Alison and   St John's House, Garrigill, Alston,
  David Hymers   Cumbria CA9 3DS
Telephone   **01434 381875** Fax 01434 382035
Rooms   2 double + 3 twin *(all en-suite)*
B&B   £20.00-£24.00
Evening meal   From £4.00   Packed lunch £3.00
(No smoking please in some areas.) **3 Crowns.** *"We can receive you in Garrigill (or Alston), provide a cup of tea, use of indoor swimming pool and sauna, free transport between Garrigill and Alston, and return in the morning."* **(Please see Cumberland Hotel Alston advertisement on page 92.)**

NENTHEAD

Nenthead from Garrigill Road

Nestling in the bowl of its surrounding hills, Nenthead is one of the highest villages in England. It was the most important lead-mining centre in the North Pennines from the beginning of 18th-c. Lead was probably discovered very early by accident when local farmers used fire to crack the stone in order to build walls around their land. It was found that a substance in the rock melted and could be formed into useful vessels. Much later they realised that the lead had great commercial value and small drift mines were opened.

The Quaker born London Lead Mining Company contributed enormously to the welfare of all the local inhabitants as well as the miners. The Company gradually provided Nenthead with all the social services such as schools, chapels, shops, a reading room, village hall and houses. The 'Miners Arms' regularly had its rent reduced as trade diminished due to the miners "preferring books to beer"! Obviously the Quaker influence was a healthy one!

Nenthead Tourist Information

PLACES OF INTEREST

Mines Heritage Centre   Excellent visitor centre with refreshments and Bunk House

EATING OUT

The Crown Inn   Has a paddock at back for campers (please put donation in box!)
01434 381271

The Miners Arms   Bunk House 01434 381427
Mines Heritage Centre Café   01434 382037

BIKE REPAIRS

The Miners Arms   Phone 01434 381427 for contacts

Carting lead

Nenthead

Mrs Hellen Sherlock
Cherry Tree, Nenthead, Alston, Cumbria CA9 3P

Telephone **01434 381434**

Rooms: 2 double + 2 family + 1 single

B&B £14.50   Packed lunch £3.00

Distance from C2C 200 yards   Pub nearby

"Stonebuilt farmhouse in pleasant surroundings. 2 bathrooms with electric showers and individual shower rooms, full central heating. Lock-up for bikes in barn."

Ann and Bob Armstrong
Foulardrigg, Nenthead, Alston, Cumbria CA9 3LP

Telephone **01434 382609**

Rooms: 1 double + 1 twin *(no smoking please)*

B&B £15.00   Packed lunch £2.50

Distance from C2C ¾ mile   Pub ¾ mile

"Save Black Hill for tomorrow! Restore batteries, and enjoy the warmth and comfort of our old farmhouse. Hearty breakfast, home-made bread."

The Miners Arms
Nenthead, Alston, Cumbria CA9 3PF

Telephone **01434 381427**

Rooms: double, family, twin, single

B&B £15.00

Bunkhouse   Sleeps 12   B&B £10.00

Evening meals   From £4.00   Packed lunch £3.25

Distance from C2C On route   Stamping Post

(No smoking in bedrooms or bunkhouse please.) *"Friendly family pub offering cheap, homely accommodation. National prize-winning menu. Home-made food and real ale. Bike spares available."* ***(See advertisement on page 93.)***

Nenthead

Nenthead Mines Heritage Centre	Nenthead, Alston, Cumbria CA9 3PD
	Telephone/Fax **01434 382037**
Bunkhouse	Sleeps 9
B&B	£12.00
Distance from C2C	On route Pub nearby

"Bunkhouse accommodation in 18th-c cottage with washing and showering facilities. Very interesting location, near village centre."

After leaving Nenthead the route rises up to Black Hill (the highest spot on the C2C). The Central Pennines have their own unique windswept and desolate beauty. Your journey now takes you through some of the wildest and loneliest moorland before it drops down into the welcoming hamlet of Allenheads.

Far from the city's ceaseless hum
And haunts of busy men,
No sounds but those of nature come
Within thy quiet glen.

On every side stretch moor and fell
In heathery garb arrayed,
Where thou dost nestle in the dell
As in a basin laid.

From "To Nenthead" by H. Jackson.

ALLENHEADS

Allenheads, reputed to be England's highest village, would have looked very different 100 years ago. A valley filled with tone- less grey slag heaps and shrouded by the smog from miners' cottage fires would have greeted you. Today this friendly little hamlet, almost hidden in pine trees, welcomes you off the moor with its babbling beck and good places to eat and rest. Allenheads once supplied a sixth of Britain's lead until cheap foreign imports brought tumbling prices and an end to the vil- lage's mining prosperity.

PLACES OF INTEREST
Heritage Centre	*In the midst of the village.*
Old Blacksmith's Shop	*Displays of local items.*

PLACES TO EAT
The Henmel Café	*Welcoming oasis for the tired, wet and hungry cyclist.*
The Village Shop	*Has a good supply of food as well as basic essentials for your bike.*
The Allenheads Inn	*An experience not to be missed!*

Allenheads

Peter & Linda Stenson　　The Allenheads Inn, Allenheads,
Hexham, Northumberland NE47 9HJ
Telephone　　**01434 685200**
Internet　　www.bta.org.UK/CYCLING
Rooms　　10 double
B&B　　£21.50-£25.00
Evening meal　　From £4.50
Distance from C2C　　On route　　Pub

*"Eccentric and entertaining, but with high standards. Comfortable en-suite rooms. Tasty food and fine ales. Featured in the Good Pub Guide 1998."***(See advertisement on page 94.)**

Helen Ratcliffe and Alan Smith　　The Old School House, Allenheads,
Northumberland NE47 9HR
Telephone/Fax　　**01434 685040**
e-mail　　headalan@aol.com
Rooms　　1 family room (sleeps 1-4)
+ 1 spacious room for larger groups
B&B　　£10.00-£13.50
Evening meal　　Available
Distance from C2C　　On route　　Pub nearby

"A friendly, colourful and unusual place. Superb dinner and tremendous breakfast, best so far on route. Great atmosphere, unrivalled views. Altogether a wonderful place to stay!" (Quotes from C2C'ers)

The Allenheads Trust, Allenheads Heritage Centre, Allenheads Northumberland NE47 9UQ. Telephone **01434 685395**. Bunkhouse accommodation. **(See advertisement on page 97.)**

Allenheads

Allenheads Lodge Outdoor Centre, Allenheads Village, Northumberland NE47 9HW. Telephone/Fax **01434 685374.** 22 beds in 4 dormitory bedrooms. Breakfast, evening meals and self-catering options available. Large groups welcome. Back-up transport + full C2C package on request. Prices start from £8.25 pp pn. On C2C route. Pub nearby. *(No smoking in bedrooms please.)* *(**See advertisement on page 96.**)*

Spring House, Allenheads, Northumberland NE47 9HJ Telephone **01434 685301** *(**See advertisement on page 97.**)*

Blanchland

Mrs Sue Clutterbuck	Townfield Country House, Townfield, Blanchland, Co Durham DH8 9UW
Telephone	**01434 675220** Fax 01434 675052
Rooms	1 double + 1 twin + 1 family
B&B	From £18.50
Evening meal	£12.00 *(prior notice please)*
Packed lunch	£4.50 Pub 2½ miles

(No smoking please.) "Beautiful historic listed family home, extensive gardens set in the hills with stunning views over Derwent Reservoir. Drying facilities, secure bicycle storage, tents welcome."

Lapwings

ROOKHOPE

This little-visited settlement welcomes you after a gloroious two miles free-wheel ride from the last summit. Rookhope keeps the secret of its hiding place well guarded as it nestles far from sight high above the Weardale Valley. It is hard to imagine that this little group of dwellings was a hive of activity only a few years

ago. In its heyday it supported a surgery, a resident district nurse, vicar, policeman, teashops, several crowded pubs and a busy school. The miners of lead, iron and fluorspar, smelting and railways totally dominated people's lives with clockwork regularity. Today the vilage is a welcome watering hole and resting place for weary cyclists before the final leg of the C2C journey down to the NE coast.

There is an **information centre** at **Rookhope Nurseries**, and a **pub, village shop and several guest-houses**.

Rookhope

Lintzgarth Arch

Lintzgarth Arch stands enormous, abandoned and out of place on the valley floor on the approach to Rookhope. The arch carried a horizontal chimney across the valley which replaced the more conventional vertical type when it was realised that a lot of lead literally went up with the smoke. Consequently young chimney sweeps were employed to scrape the valuable lead and silver deposits from the chimney once a week. A dangerous job done by youngsters long before the days of Health and Safety!

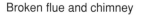

Broken flue and chimney

Rookhope

Mrs June Pringle
Boltsburn House, Rookhope, Co Durham DL13 2BG

Telephone **01388 517414**
Rooms 3 double + 1 single
B&B £14.00 Packed lunch £2.50
Distance from C2C On route Pub nearby

"Large detatched house, spacious rooms with colour TV, tea/coffee-making facilities, bath and shower. Right next to Rookhope Inn. Garage for bikes. Drying facilities."

Mike and Kay Leathers
Garden Cottage, 7 Front Street, Rookhope, Bishop Auckland DL13 2AZ

Telephone **01388 517577**
Rooms 1 double + 1 twin + 1 fam.(4) + 1 single
B&B £16.00
Evening meal £6.00 Packed lunch £2.50
Distance from C2C On route Pub nearby

(*No smoking in bedrooms please.*) *"Stone-built cottage with beamed ceilings, open fires, guests' lounge, TV and tea/coffee-making facilities in bedrooms, 4 bathrooms (one with a Jacuzzi), drying facilities, garage for bikes."*

Mr and Mrs Steve Thompson
The Rookhope Inn, Rookhope, Weardale, Co. Durham DL13 2BG

Telephone **01388 517215**
Rooms 1 double + 1 family + 1 twin
B&B £16.00-£20.00
Evening meal From £3.50 Packed lunch £3.50
Distance from C2C On route Pub

"Large detached Inn with lounge, pool and dining rooms. Real beams and open fires. In 1997 and 1998 Good Beer Guides."

Rookhope

Janette and Tony Newbon	High Brandon, Rookhope, Weardale, Co. Durham, DL13 2AF
Telephone	**01388 517673**
Rooms	1 single + 1 twin + 1 family
B&B	£14.00-£16.00
Evening Meal	£5.00-£10.00
Packed lunch	£3.00
Distance from C2C	On route Pub 1 mile

(No smoking please.) "A delightful stone-built period farmhouse B&B, with magnificent views of Weardale. Facilities include TV, en-suite room, drying facilities, separate lounge. Will provide lift to pub."

Breaking and washing iron-ore

STANHOPE

You may wish to cycle via Stanhope, an attractive Weardale village nestling between the Northern Dales. The village expanded in 1845 when the Stanhope & Tyne Railway was constructed. A standing engine hauled the heavy wagons up Crawley Side. It then continued on its journey down the Waskerley Way to Consett and Cleveland.

PLACES OF INTEREST

Dales Visitor Centre Town centre 01388 527650

**Fossil tree at St
  Thomas's Church** 350 million years old, found in 1914 in an Edmundbyers mine

EATING OUT

Stanhope Old Hall A la carte menu 01388 528 451

Various pubs All in town centre

CYCLE SHOPS

**Weardale Mountain
  Bikes** Frosterley 01388 528129 (within 5 miles of C2C)

*C2C Features: the route leads you up Crawley Side, aptly named due to its steep incline, and on up to the **Waskerley Way**. Before the railways were built, all raw materials were transported by pack horses. Teams of tough little Galloway horses would pick their way across the wind-swept Pennines and then down into the valleys. The lead horse often had a bell attached to his harness to aid the following horses across the mist-cloaked moors.*

Stanhope

Mr and Mrs Storey Queen's Head Hotel, 89 Front Street,
Stanhope, Weardale   DL13 2UB

Telephone	**01388 528160**
Rooms	4 twin
B&B	£17.00
Evening meal	From £2.60 Packed lunch £3.00
Distance from C2C	c. 1 mile Hotel has Public Bar

"Small family-run country pub, full licence, fine real ales. All rooms have colour TV and tea/coffee-making facilities."

Mrs E. Hamilton Red Lodge Guest House, 2 Market
Place, Stanhope, DL13 2UN

Telephone	**01388 527851**
Rooms	2 double + 1 single
B&B	£17.50-£19.00
Distance from C2C	c.1 mile Pub nearby

"Family run guest-house, well equipped with TV and tea/coffee-making facilities in all rooms, some en-suite. Pubs and fast food take-aways nearby."

James Elder Stanhope Old Hall, Stanhope,
Weardale, Co. Durham DL13 2PF

Telephone	**01388 528451** Fax 01388 527795
Rooms	10 rooms (double, single + family) B&B From £35.00
Evening meal	Available Packed lunch available
Distance from C2C	c. 1 mile Pubs nearby

"Stanhope Old Hall is a medieval hunting lodge with an old-world atmosphere. Fully-licensed with bar and restaurant meals. Special rates for C2C."

CONSETT

As the C2C approaches Consett it passes the site of the Old Consett Steel Works which originally opened in 1837. It was eventually closed and the enormous site was dismantled in 1980. This ghost-like empty space of 700 acres now looks strange and desolate after those Dickensian years when the night skies glowed bright with fires from hungry steel blast-furnaces.

PLACES OF INTEREST

Phileas Fogg Factory   Alias Derwent Valley Foods

Shotley Bridge   An old spa town, well-known for German sword-makers in the 17th-c

EATING OUT

Grey Horse   Real Ales brewed on the premises! Light lunches and right on C2C route. **(See advertisement on page 98.)**

Jolly Drovers Pub   Leadgate 01207 503 994

CYCLE SHOPS

Consett Cycle Co   62 Medomsley Rd 01207 581 205

McVickers Sports   Front Street 01207 505 121

C2C Features: dotted along the line are story-boards set on vertical sleepers which interpret the history of the railway. These are chapters taken from a novel, The Celestial Railroad, *by John Downie. It is available from Sustrans North Eastern Office at Stanley, 01207 281259.*

Castleside

Liz Lawson

Bee Cottage Farm, Castleside, Consett, Co. Durham DH8 9HW

Telephone **01207 508224**

Rooms 5 double + 3 family + 1 single

B&B From £22.00

Evening meal £13.50 Packed lunch £4.50

Distance from C2C 3 fields away!

(No smoking please.) **ETB 2 Crowns Highly Commended.**

"Working farm with lovely views, situated close to the Waskerley Way (between points 107 and 108 on C2C map). Sleeps 34. Warm welcome, home comforts, good food and plenty of it. Tearoom open 1pm-6pm all summer." **(See advertisement on page 95.)**

Noel and Jane Rekl

Castleside Inn, Staniford-Dam, Consett, Co. Durham DH8 8EP

Telephone **01207 581443** Fax 01207 583373

Internet http://www.scoot.co.uk/castleside

Rooms 1 single + 4 double + 2 twin + 1 family

B&B £17.95-£26.95 *(10% discount for C2C)*

Meals available 11.00am-10.30pm

Packed lunch Available on request

Distance from C2C 600 yds Public bar

"Rural setting very near C2C route. Quality accommodation, all en-suite. Secure cycle housing. Play area." **(See advertisement on page 99.)**

STANLEY

Stanley is set on a breezy hill top and commands a bird's eye view of the whole area. **Sustrans North Eastern Office** *is at Rockwood House, Barn Hill, Stanley, Co. Durham DH9 8AN. Tel: 01207 281259, Fax 01207 281113. Information on other Sustrans Bike Routes is available here together with interesting booklets and C2C T-shirts. You may join the Sustrans Charity here. They are responsible for creating a UK cycle-way network.*

PLACES OF INTEREST
Tanfield Railway	World's oldest operating railway!
Beamish	Open-air museum

EATING OUT
Hill Top Restaurant	East Street 01207 233217
Asda	On ring road, Coffee Shop
Shafto's Bar	S Causey Farm 01207 235555

CYCLE SHOPS
Main Brothers	Front Street 01207 290258

***C2C Features:** **Beamish Museum** is England's largest open-air museum and has a working steam railway, trams, a Victorian town centre, a demonstration colliery, a school and a working farm. The C2C route passes within yards of the entrance gate.*

Stanley

Mrs Pamela   Bushblades Farm, Harperley,
Gibson   nr Stanley, Co. Durham DH9 9UA
Telephone   **01207 232722**
Rooms   2 double + 1 twin
B&B   £16.00-£18.50
Distance from C2C   ¾ mile   Pub ¾ mile
(No smoking please.) **ETB Listed, Commended, AA QQ.**
"Comfortable Georgian farmhouse, large garden, colour TV and tea/coffee-making facilities in all rooms, some en-suite."

Beamish Open Air Museum

Beamish

Joanne Taylor Beamish Mary Inn, No Place, Beamish, Co. Durham DH9 0QH
Telephone **0191 370 0237** Fax 0191 370 0091
Rooms 3 double + 1 triple
B&B £17.00-£20.00
Evening meal From £3.75 Packed lunch from £2.50
Distance from C2C ½ mile Pub
ETB 3 Crowns. *"Traditional Inn. Specialises in good food, real ale, live music. Comfortable atmosphere. All rooms with private facilities. (Landlord and landlady both keen cyclists.)"*

Rowlands Gill

G. Wetherspoon Towneley Arms Hotel, Station Road, Rowlands Gill, Tyne & Wear NE39 1QF
Telephone **01207 542274** Fax 01207 542523
Rooms 17 double + 17 single *(all en-suite)*
B&B £35.00-£60.00
Evening meal Available Packed lunch available
Distance from C2C On route Hotel has Public Bar
"Very near Newcastle city centre, pleasant surroundings. Tea/coffee-making facilities, hair dryer and colour TV in all rooms."

CHESTER-LE-STREET

Chester-le-Street is the oldest town in County Durham, and was once a Roman settlement. The Washington Wildfowl and Wetlands Centre is very near the route. This 100-acre water-fowl park designed by Peter Scott has over 1,200 birds and is visited by several mammals including the scarce water vole.

PLACES OF INTEREST
The Washington Wetlands Trust 100 acres of magnificent parkland, ponds and hides 0191 416 5454

EATING OUT
The Wheatsheaf Pelaw Grange 0191 388 3104
The Barley Mow Browns Buildings 0191 410 4504

CYCLE SHOPS
Cestria Cycles 11 Ashfield Terrace - 0191 388 7535

*C2C Features: the Penshaw monument, a look-alike Doric Temple dedicated to Theseus, was built in memory of John George Lambton, the 1st Earl of Durham. Be thankful to leave the river here for fear of the **Lambton Worm**. The legend runs that a young Lambton lad, fishing in the river against all advice, caught a small worm. In disgust he threw it into a nearby well and went off to fight in the Crusades. On his return the "worm" had grown into a dragon which ravaged the countryside. A witch agreed to slay the beast on condition that Lambton kill the first living thing he met. Unfortunately it was his father, whom of course he spared, and so failed to fulfil his side of the bargain, thus nine generations of Lambtons were condemned to meet untimely ends!*

Chester-le-Street

Lambton Worm Hotel

	52 North Road, Chester-le-Street, Co. Durham DH3 4AT
Telephone	**0191 388 3386**
Rooms	9 double + 4 single
B&B	£16.00-£28.00
Evening meals	£2.50-£15.00
Packed lunch	£3.50
Distance from C2C	On route Hotel has Public Bar

ETB 2 Crowns. *"13-bedroomed hotel/pub boasting 2 bars, excellent food, pool, darts, big-screen football. Tolerant understanding staff of muddy and exhausted bikers!"*

Mrs Heather Rippon

	Malling Guest House, 1 Oakdale Ter. Newfield, Chester-le-Street, DH2 2SV
Telephone	**0191 370 2571**
Rooms	1 double + 1 single + 1 fam. *(sleeps 4)*
B&B	£16.00-£25.00
Evening meals	From £2.50 *(in pub over the road)*
Packed lunch	From: £2.50
Distance from C2C	⅓ mile Pub nearby

1 Crown Commended. *"Previously a doctor's house with surgery. Good views to the rear. Heather is a renowned good story-teller! Warm and friendly atmosphere."*

SUNDERLAND

*Sunderland, once home of shipbuilding, coal-mining and glass making, became a city in 1992 and is just a stone's throw from the coast and the North Sea. **St Peter's Church**, built in 674 when Sunderland became established as one of England's earliest centres of Christianity, was notable as the first "glazed" building in England. George Washington's ancestral home is in **Washington village,** which is now part of the city of Sunderland: what an amazing connection with Whitehaven, the start of the C2C, where Washington's grandparents had their home!*

PLACES OF INTEREST

Washington Old Hall
In Washington village. George Washington's ancestral home 0191 416 6879

St Andrew's Church Roker
Known as the "Cathedral of William Morris's Arts and Crafts movement"

Crowtree Leisure Centre
Town centre: have a celebratory swim - the sea could be a bit chilly! 0191 553 2600

EATING OUT

Swallow Hotel Seaburn
On the seafront: has an à la carte menu 0191 529 2041

Seaburn Leisure Centre
Good café 0191 529 4091

CYCLE SHOPS

Peter Darke Cycles
113 High St West 0191 510 8155

For tourist and accommodation information on Newcastle, Tynemouth and Whitley Bay please turn to pages 112 - 115

Sunderland

Karen & Robin Dawson Belmont Guest House, 8 St Georges Terrace, Roker, Sunderland SR6 9LX
Telephone **0191 567 2438**
Rooms 10 double + 2 single
B&B £16.00-£28.00
Evening meal £5.00 Packed lunch £2.50
Distance from C2C On route Pub nearby

ETB 2 Crowns. *"Small family-run licensed guest-house. 100 yds from sea front and C2C route. En-suite rooms. Lock-up available for bikes. Warm welcome is assured."*

Mrs Eileen Hughes Brendon House, 49 Roker Park Road, Roker, Sunderland SR6 9PL
Telephone **0191 548 9303**
Rooms 3 double + 4 family + 1 single
B&B £13.50-£14.50
Evening meal £5.75 Packed lunch £3.25
Distance from C2C ½ mile Pub nearby

1 Crown Approved. *"5 minutes from Marine Centre and Railway Station. Clean, comfortable, spacious rooms with TV, tea/coffee making facilities. Ideal for weary travellers. Reductions for children. Bike storage."*

Stan Jenkins Roker View Guest House, 2 Benedict Road, Roker, Sunderland SR6 0PE
Telephone **0191 510 8325** (day)/**514 0816** (pm)
Rooms 2 double + 3 twin + 2 family + 1 single
B&B £13.00-£15.00
Distance from C2C On route Pubs nearby

"Next to Harbour View pub. Restaurants and pubs nearby. 2 minutes from start/finish point. Secure parking for cars and bikes. Satellite TV. Tea/coffee and colour TV in all rooms. A very warm welcome is guaranteed for all fellow cyclists."

Camping & Caravans Sites

Workington/Whitehaven
Inglenook Caravan & Camping Park, Fitz Bridge, Lamplugh, Workington, CA14 4SH *(on C2C)* Tel/Fax **01946 861240**

Braithwaite
Scotgate Chalet, Camping & Caravan Holiday Park, Braithwaite, Keswick, Cumbria CA12 5TF *(C2C 100 yds)* Tel **017687 78343** *(See advertisement page 87.)*

Troutbeck
Gill Head Farm, Troutbeck, Penrith, Cumbria CA11 0ST Tel **017687 79652** *(See advertisement page 86.)*

Penruddock
Beckses Caravan & Camping Park, Penruddock, Penrith, Cumbria CA11 0RX *(c. ° mile from C2C)* Tel **017684 83224**

Alston
Horse & Waggon Camping & Caravan Park, Nentsberry, Alston, Cumbria CA9 3LH, William Patterson *(swings on play area, WC and showers available, 3 miles south-east Alston on A689. Tents from £4.00, OS map ref NY 764 451)* Tel **01434 382805**

Hamsterley
Byreside Caravan Site, Hamsterley, Newcastle-upon-Tyne NE17 7RT, Mrs Val Clemitson *(between Ebchester and Hamsterley Mill, adjacent to Derwent Walk & Cycle Track)* Tel **01207 560280/560499**

Camping & Caravans Sites

Rowlands Gill
Derwent Park Caravan & Camping Site, Rowlands Gill, Tyne & Wear NE39 1LG. David Johnson *(discount for C2C cyclists. 100m from C2C Route)*
Tel/Fax **01207 543383** *(See advertisement page 103.)*

Beamish
Bobby Shafto Caravan Park, Beamish, Co. Durham DH9 0RY *(adjacent to world famous Beamish Museum, only ¾ mile from C2C route)*
Tel **0191 370 1776** Fax 0191 456 1083

Youth Hostels

YHA, Northern Region, PO Box 11, Matlock, Derbyshire DE4 2XA (inc SAE)
Tel **01629 825850** *(See advertisement page 103)*

Cockermouth Youth Hostel
Double Mills, Cockermouth, Cumbria CA13 0DS
£4.95 (under 18's) £7.20 (adults) + Breakfast £2.95 Evening meal £4.40 *(on C2C route)*
Tel **01900 822561**

Skiddaw House Youth Hostel
Bassenthwaite, Keswick, Cumbria CA12 4QX
£3.85 (under 18's) £5.65 (adults), self-catering only
Tel **016974 78325**

Keswick Youth Hostel

Station Road, Keswick, Cumbria CA12 5LH
£6.55 (under 18s) £9.75 (adults) + Breakfast £2.95 *Membership requirement: available at Hostel. (on C2C route)*
Tel **017687 72484**

Alston Youth Hostel

The Firs, Alston, Cumbria CA9 3RW £5.40 (under 18s) £8.00 (adults) + Breakfast £2.95 *(2 miles from C2C route)*
Tel **01434 381509** Fax 01434 382401

Alston Training & Adventure Centre

High Plains Lodge, Alston, Cumbria CA9 3DD From £6.50
Tel **01434 381886**

Edmundbyers Youth Hostel

Low House, Edmundbyers, Consett, Co Durham DH8 9NL
£4.45 (under 18s) £6.50 (adults), self-catering only (o*n C2C route)* Tel/Fax **01207 255651**

Consett YMCA

Parliament Street, Consett, Co. Durham DH8 5DH 12 rooms, 65 beds in Alpine style rooms. B&B £12.50. Evening meal £5.00. Packed lunch £3.00. Residential license. Pubs nearby. OS Ref. 105 509. *(See advertisement page 102.)*
Tel **01207 502680/501852**, Fax 01207 501578

Newcastle upon Tyne Youth Hostel

107 Jesmond Road, Newcastle upon Tyne NE2 1NJ
£5.15 (under 18s) £7.70 (adults) + Breakfast £2.85
Tel **0191 281 2570**

Camping Barns

Camping Barns are stone barns providing simple overnight shelter. They are roomy and dry, so there is no need to carry a tent. They have a wooden sleeping platform sometimes with mattresses. Tables, a slate cooking bench and cold water tap and WC are also provided together with a washing-up bowl, clothes hooks and waste bags.

Cumbria: for bookings at these Lake District National Park barns you must first ring Keswick Information Centre on **017687 72803**

Swallow Barn, Waterend Farm *(west end of Loweswater, on C2C route)* OS NY 116 226

Catbells Barn, Newlands Valley *(c. 2 miles from C2C route)* OS NY 243 208

Eagle's Nest Barn, Low Grove Farm, Millbeck, Keswick, *(c. 2 miles from C2C route)* OS NY 258 259

Blake Beck Barn, Mungrisdale, between Keswick and Penrith, *(c. 2 miles from C2C route)* OS NY 367 278

Alston - Wearhead Camping Barn, Black Cleugh, Cowshill, Wearhead, Co. Durham DL13 1DJ *(c. 2 miles from C2C route)* Tel **01388 537 395** Mr Robert Walton OS NY 436 821

Useful Telephone Numbers

Weather News

Cumbria & the Lake District Weathercall	0891 500 419
North East England Weathercall	0891 500 418

Tourist Information Centres

Whitehaven	01946 695678
Keswick	017687 72645
Cockermouth	01900 822634
Penrith	01768 867466
Alston (April to October)	01434 381696
Stanhope	01388 527650
Beamish	0191 370 2533
Gateshead	0191 477 3478
Sunderland	0191 553 2000
Newcastle upon Tyne	0191 261 0610
Whitley Bay	0191 200 8535

Travel Information: Bus, Coach and Train

Stagecoach Cumberland	01946 63222
Cumbria County Council Travellink	01228 606000
Durham County Council Travellink	0191 383 3337
Tyne & Wear County Council Travellink	0191 232 5325
National Express	0990 808080
National Express Newcastle	0191 232 3300
National Rail Enquiries Line	0345 484 950
Scotrail Enquiries Line	0345 550 033
Cycle Booking Line NW Trains	0161 228 5906

Bike Shops and Repairs

Whitehaven	Kershaw's Cycles, 125 Queen St 01946 590700
	Mark Taylor Cycles, 5/6 New St 01946 692252
Workington	Traffic Lights Bikes, 35 Washington St 01900 603283
	New Bike Shop, 18-20 Market Pl 01900 603337
Cockermouth	Wordsworth Hotel Bike Hire 01900 822757
	Derwent Cycles, 4 Market Place 01900 822113
Braithwaite	The Stores 017687 78273
Keswick	Keswick Mountain Bikes, Southey Hill 017687 75202
Penrith	Arragons, 2 Brunswick Rd 01768 890344
	Harpers, 1-2 Middlegate 01768 864475
Alston	Nentholme B&B, The Butts 01434 381 523
Allenheads	Village Shop: essential bike spares
Stanhope	Weardale Mountain Bikes, Frosterley 01388 528129
Consett	Consett Cycle Co, 62 Medomsley Rd 01207 581 205
	McVickers Sports, Front St 01207 505 121
Stanley	Main Brothers, Front St 01207 290 258
Chester-le-St	Cestria Cycles, 11 Ashfield Terr 0191 3887535
Washington	Bike Shed, 3 Westview, Concord 0191 416 906
	Bike Rack, 65-66 In Shops 0191 419 1521
Metro Centre	The Bike Place, 8 Allison Court 0191 488 3137
Newcastle	Newcastle Cycle Centre, 165 Westgate Rd 0191 230 3022
	Dentons, Blenheim St 0191 232 3903
Byker	Hardisty Cycles, 5 Union Rd 0191 265 8619
Sunderland	Darke Cycles, 113 High St W 0191 510 8155
	Cycle World, 118 High St West 0191 565 8188

C2C Check List

Bike

Chain splitter
Pump
Allen keys
Adjustable wrench
Screwdriver
Tyre levers
Spoke key
Front/rear lights
Rear view mirror
Panniers

Bike Spares

Inner tube
Puncture repair kit
Front and rear lights
Batteries
Spare chain links
Brake blocks
Straddle wire
Bike lock

Personal Kit

Wash kit
Money / credit card
Head torch
First-aid kit
Liners for bags
Emergency rations
Maps & B&B Guide
Water bottle
Good book

Clothing

Cycle shorts (padded)
Cycle shirt
Thermal vest
Helmet
Gloves
Fleece
Windproof top
Waterproof jacket
Waterproof trousers
Boots/shoes & socks
Lightweight trousers
Lightweight trainers
Towel
Underwear

Morven House Hotel
Siddick Road
Workington
Cumbria
CA14 1LE
Tel/Fax 01900 602118

Relaxed and informal atmosphere for guests. En-suite rooms. Good food. Ideal stop over for C2C participants. Start your tour in comfortable, detached house with car park and secure cycle storage. You may leave your car until your return if you wish.

The Waverley Hotel
Tangier Street, Whitehaven,
Cumbria CA28 7UX
Tel 01946 694337

*A handsome 300-year-old hotel in the centre of historic Whitehaven. Convenient for the start of the C2C and close to the railway and bus station. Excellent home-made meals are served in a fully-licensed bar or restaurant. Twins, doubles, family and single rooms are available. **Discounts for group bookings**. Secure parking for cycles and cars.*

Proprietors: Richard and Cheryl Twinn

Glenlea House, Whitehaven

Don't miss the opportunity to sit on our terrace with an evening drink and enjoy magnificent views stretching as far as the eye can see from the harbour to the Isle of Man. We will take care of your car while you are away.

Mrs Oliver, Glenlea House, Lowca, Whitehaven,
Cumbria CA28 6PS Tel 01946 693873 Fax 01946 694350

Gill Head Farm

Mrs J. Wilson
Gill Head Farm
Troutbeck
Penrith
Cumbria CA11 0ST
Tel 017687 79652

Bed and Breakfast + Camping. Stay in the comfortable 17th-century farmhouse with oak beams and log fires. Enjoy traditional home-cooking. All rooms are en-suite, with tea/coffee-making facilities, colour TV, and central heating throughout. For campers we have a level, sheltered campsite, with laundry and shop. The Troutbeck Inn is a 5 minute walk - bike no further!

Chalets, Camping & Caravans
HOLIDAY PARK
Proprietors: Stuart Bros.
Peacefully situated between Bassenthwaite Lake
and Derwentwater with easy access
to all areas of Lakeland

CARAVANS & CHALETS TO LET
Fully Equipped   Toilet   Shower
Colour Television

SITE FOR TOURING CARAVANS
Electric Hook-ups
Licensed Tent Site adjoining
AMENITIES
Wash Toilet Shower Block   Shaver Points   Hair Dryers
Licensed Shop   Laundry   Café / Coffee Shop
Cycle Compound

Please send S.A.E. for brochure
SCOTGATE CHALET, CAMPING &
CARAVAN HOLIDAY PARK
Braithwaite, Keswick, Cumbria CA12 5TF
Tel   017687 78343

ARRAGONS CYCLE CENTRE
2 Brunswick Road
Penrith

Your Coast to Coast Cycle Shop
For spares, repairs, wheel-building
and wheel repairs

Main agents for
**MARIN SARACEN DAWES M-TRAX
RALEIGH**

Any problems at all,
just give us a call

01768   890344

Home Farm

Mrs Jane Metcalfe
Home Farm
Edenhall
Penrith
Cumbria CA11 8SS
Tel 01768 881203

A home-from-home atmosphere welcomes you onto this working Eden Valley farm in the quiet village of Edenhall. Spacious rooms with tea/coffee-making facilities and a deep bath await you at the end of a long day on your bike. There is a large and warm visitors lounge. The Edenhall Hotel serves excellent bar meals and also has an à la carte restaurant - it is only a very short walk for those with weary legs.

Langley House
Bed & Breakfast

HIGHLY COMMENDED
Listed

A friendly welcome awaits weary cyclists at Langley House. Warm, spacious, attractively furnished bedrooms, comfortable beds and generous breakfasts. Make Langwathby your over-night stop before the climb up to Hartside Summit. Overlooking the village green, we provide locked cycle storage, washing/drying service and packed lunches. The village inn serves meals. (NO SMOKING PLEASE)

Langley House, Langwathby,   **Mrs Lorna Egan**
Penrith, Cumbria CA10 1LW   **01768 881571**

ST PAUL'S MISSION
ALSTON

Open from 1st April 1998, St Paul's Mission is a facility custom made for C2C participants in a converted Chapel.

Our range of indoor amenities include:
Bunk-bed accommodation for 36 guests (bunk-beds in separate cubicles), large showering and WC facilities, indoor bike security room, washing and drying room, sauna, kitchen with cooking facilities, food and drinks available, lounge with pool table, TV, full central heating.

Rates

Bed only	£10.00
Bed (sleeping bag + pillow)	£15.00

Please book ahead: **St Paul's Mission**
Town Head   Alston   CA9 3SG
01768 862951 or Fax 01768 896747

THE
CUMBERLAND HOTEL
ALSTON

Townfoot, Alston, Cumbria CA9 3HX

We offer a complete package of assistance for C2C cyclists and support groups. This includes:

Full Bed & Breakfast facilities with all bedrooms having full en-suite facilities and three being "family" rooms to take 3-4 people each.

Prices from £20.00 to £24.00 with lunch and dinner available from a bar or restaurant menu (£4.00 upwards) with a high quality and exciting variety.
Packed lunch available £3.00.
Bike storage, drying room and cleaning facilities.
Bunk House being built Spring '98.

Fully licensed, with two bars (one for residents and diners) with extensive views of the River South Tyne.
Large car park next to hotel.
Non-smoking restaurant and residents' lounge.

If you are cycling through Garrigill, we can collect you from St Johns House (see full entry in Garrigill listing), storing bikes there, and take you "free" to Alston to sleep, enjoy a rest and look round the town, then return you to your bike. Residents are able to use our large nearby indoor swimming pool and sauna for a small fee as the perfect way to ease their aches and pains.

Phone 01434 381875 for bookings or **Fax 01434 382035**

The Miners Arms

At 1500' above sea level, the Miners Arms can probably lay claim to be the highest village pub in England. If you like excellent food (national prize winning cuisine), great beer (guest ales changed weekly) and friendly family hospitality or you just like drinking at altitude - then you must try THE MINERS ARMS in Nenthead - it's well worth a visit.

Accommodation - Bunkhouse which sleeps 12 (four 3-high bunks), with washing and changing facilities which include 2 sinks and 2 shower/toilet rooms. All bedding is provided, but there are **NO** cooking facilities. Family, double, twin and single accommodation is available for Bed & Breakfast in the main house. Each room has colour TV. Tea/coffee are available on request.

It is the official **Stamping Post** in Nenthead for the C2C Cycle Route. A comprehensive selection of bicycle spares are available. Open all day May - September.

Please contact The Miners Arms, Nenthead, Alston, Cumbria CA9 3PF Tel 01434 381427

BEE COTTAGE FARM

**CASTLESIDE CONSETT
CO. DURHAM DH8 9HW**
Tel Liz Lawson 01207 508224
**Farmhouse Teas
Bed & Breakfast
Self-catering**

A working farm with lovely views situated close to
the Waskerley Way
(between points 107 and 108 on the C2C map.)

Evening Meals and Packed Lunches available
Tea-Room open 1 - 6pm
Good food - plenty of it!
A warm, friendly welcome and home comforts
for individual cyclists, family groups
or even larger parties
Sleeps 34

The "Wish You Were
Here" TV team stayed
with us whilst in the area
when making the C2C
film - *We hope you will
too!*

English Tourist Board
HIGHLY COMMENDED

Highly Commended

95

The Grey Horse

Consett

Paul & Rosaleen Conroy
115 Sherburn Terrace
Consett
Co. Durham
DH8 6NE

01207 502585

*A traditional warm and friendly welcome
awaits you at the Grey Horse
Home of Derwentrose Brewery.
All our real Ales are brewed on the
premises including our famous*
Coast 2 Coast Ale.
*Real fires.
Over 70 malt and deluxe whiskies.
Light lunches and bar snacks,
hot and cold sandwiches.*

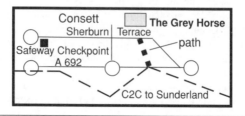

THE BIKE BUS

Cycle Collection / Delivery Service

 Sea to Sea Cycle Route
*Whitehaven or Workington
to Sunderland or Newcastle*

For further information contact
STANLEY TAXIS & MINI COACHES
Bus Station, Stanley, Co. Durham DH9 0TD
Tel (01207) 230000   Fax (01207) 233233

TYNEMOUTH STATION URBAN BOTHY

Residential accommodation within the station building conveniently situated adjacent to the main square, village centre, shops and pubs. The Metro stops at the station, giving access to Newcastle and coastal resorts.

This facility is ideally situated, being at the end of the Sea to Sea (C2C) route, at the beginning of the Reivers cycle route (return C2C), at the end/beginning of the Newcastle to Carlisle, and the Coast and Castles (Tynemouth to Berwick). The official accreditation stamp is obtained by calling at the Bothy or Porters, both within the station.

The facility provides bunk-beds, showers, WC, H & C, CH, bike store (breakfast and snacks available from adjacent Coffee Shop)

1998 price guide
Single bed, per night using own sleeping bag £9.00
Single bed, bedding provided £12.00

This new facility is open for the 1998 season. Party/group enquiries are welcome as well as individual books. For further information please send a SAE to **Ray Demesne, The Estate Office, Kirkwhelpington, Northumberland NE19 2RG Tel 01830 540342 For reservations telephone the Bothy on 0191 258 3167**

**TYNEMOUTH STATION
STATION TERRACE
TYNEMOUTH
TYNE & WEAR
NE30 4RE**

ON YOUR BIKE

The family cycling magazine

On Your Bike is for new and 'born again' cyclists. It's an award-winning cycle magazine that doesn't talk down to you, a jargon-free zone. Published three times a year – Spring, Summer and Autumn – *On Your Bike* is available in newsagents, bike shops and Halfords. At £2.75 for 160+ pages an issue it's brilliant value for money but subscribe and you save 20 percent. A one year subscription costs just £6.60 (cheques made payable to Kindlife Ltd.).

NEED ROUTE INFO? Get your hands on **The Family Cycling Sourcebook** from the publishers of **On Your Bike**. The Sourcebook is a collection of all the traffic-free way-marked cycle trails throughout the UK. All 250 of them. **The Family Cycling Sourcebook** is the essential reference for planning your weekends awheel. Available from book shops at £4.95.

**Kindlife Ltd, 6a Kenton Park Centre, Newcastle upon Tyne NE3 4NN
Tel: 0191 213 2058 Fax: 0191 213 2052**

Helpful Comments Please !

If you have the time, we would be very interested to hear from you about any aspect of the guide and accommodation - constructive criticism is welcome! We are always looking for ideas to include in next year's guide, and for that ultimate C2C holiday photo for our next front cover.

_____

_____

_____

_____

_____

_____

_____

Please post to Curlew Press, C2C, Croft House, Newton Reigny, nr Penrith, Cumbria CA11 0AY

The Reivers
Cycle Route

A cycle Route
from
Tynemouth to Whitehaven

To be used with the official route map
available from Sustrans 0117 929 0888

Gina Farncombe

Curlew Press

Contents

Route maps   110-111
Accommodation   114-139
Caravan/camping sites   141
Youth hostels   140
Tourist information   142
Bus & train information   142
Weather news   142
Bike repairs & shops   143
Cyclist's check list   82
Advertisements   144-146
How to get home   147
Comments please   106

Accommodation
place names (east-west)

Newcastle   112
Tynemouth   114
whitely Bay   114-115
Stamfordham   116
Bellingham   116-118
Greenhaugh   119
stannesburn   119
Falstone   120-122
Kielder   123-126
Newcastleton   127-129
Bewcastle   129-130
Walton   131
Catlowdy   132
Carlisle   133-134
Hesket Newmarket   136
Caldbeck   137-138
Uldale   139
Ireby   139
Cockermouth   21-23

The Reivers Cycle Route

This 150 mile cycle way runs from east to west coast with the gradients in the cyclists favour. It winds its way through some of the wildest and most untouched countryside in the UK from the mouth of the mighty River Tyne to the Cumbrian coast. Along the way riders will follow the shores of beautiful Kielder Water before crossing the border for a brief foray into Scotland.

The Route has been named after the marauding family clans who terrorised northern England and the Scottish Borders in the 15th c. and 16th c. They lived by cattle rustling, kidnapping, arson and murder! The route passes many fortified farmhouses revealing the rich heritage of the area.

The Reivers Cycle Route gives the potential of a wonderful round trip by linking with the C2C at Whitehaven.

Start your holiday from home by leaving your car behind! There are frequent main line inter-city trains to and from Newcastle.

If at all possible, please book accommodation, meals and packed lunches in advance, and do not arrive unannounced expecting beds and meals to be available! If you have to cancel a booking, please give the proprietor as much notice as you can so that the accommodation can be re-let.

Note   Back-up vehicles are strongly advised to use main roads in order to keep the Reivers Cycle Route as traffic free as possible.

REIVERS CYCLE ROUTE - WESTERN HALF

```
·········· England - Scotland border
```

N

0   10   20
km

SOUTHERN UPLANDS

M74/A74

SCOTLAND

Hermitage
Castle

Newcastleton
Kershopefoot
Bailey Mill
Catlowdy
Longtown
Hethersgill
Bewcastle
Walton

FIRTH

Silloth

ENGLAND

CARLISLE

M6

River Eden

SOLWAY

Dalston

Whelpo
Parkend
Caldbeck
Ireby
Newlands
Hesket
Newmarket
Uldale
Fell Side

MARYPORT

PENRITH

Seaton

Bassenthwaite Lake

COCKERMOUTH
WORKINGTON

KESWICK

M6

WHITEHAVEN

THE LAKE DISTRICT

```
——      main route
········  alternative route
· · · ·   Cumbria Cycleway
▸▸▸▸     C-2-C route
```

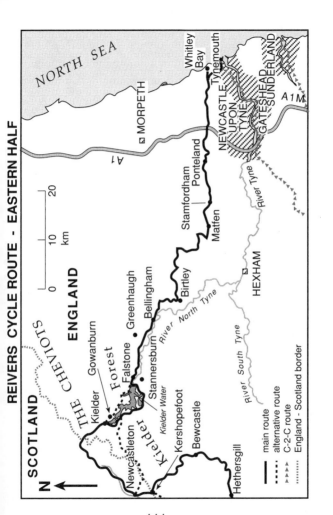

REIVERS CYCLE ROUTE - EASTERN HALF

main route
alternative route
C-2-C route
England - Scotland border

111

NEWCASTLE

Newcastle can trace its beginnings to the river-crossing and fort which we know as the start of Hadrian's Wall. Later Robert, the son of William I, built a fort in 1080 and called it Newcastle. The shipping of coal and wool played a big part in the town's growth as a merchant and trading centre, and later ship-building and engineering were to employ a large part of the community.

Earl Grey Monument

TYNEMOUTH *owes its existence to the outcrop of hard sandstone which juts out between the Tyne and the sea defying the effects of wave and weather. Monks from the Holy Island of Lindisfarne came here in 627 and built the Priory which was one of the richest in the country and at one stage in its history monks were sent here as a reprimand for being disobedient. One poor exile wrote: "Shipwrecks are frequent and the poor people eat only a malodorous seaweed called 'slank' which they gather on the*

rocks, but the church is of wondrous beauty." Later during the Roman occupation Tynemouth was an important supply port for Hadrian's Wall. In Victorian times people flocked here on the new railway to enjoy the sheltered bathing and boating.

Tynemouth Priory

NEWCASTLE

PLACES OF INTEREST
Bagpipe Museum   Unusual and interesting
Laing Art Gallery   Holds very good exhibitions

PLACES TO EAT
Crampersanda Pub   On quayside: lively atmosphere
Café Procope   On quayside: good food and
                          popular with students

BIKE SHOPS and REPAIRS
Hardisty Bikes   5 Union Road 0191 510 8155
Dentons   Blenheim St 0191 232 3903

TYNEMOUTH

PLACES OF INTEREST
The Castle and Priory   Great atmosphere
                          Sea Life Centre
                          Excellent displays

PLACES TO EAT
Land of Green Ginger   Home-made food café
Kristans   Fresh local fish, very good chips
Porters Café   Tynemouth Station

OUTDOOR EQUIPMENT
Outdoor World   Whitley Bay, good stock
                          of outdoor equipment

Tynemouth and Whitley Bay

St Mary's Lighthouse

Stuart Collingwood Avalon Hotel, 26 South Parade,
Whitley Bay, Tyne & Wear NE26 2RG

Telephone	**0191 251 0080** Fax 0191 251 0100
Rooms	3 single + 2 double + 1 twin + 8 family
B&B	£20.00-£30.00
Evening Meal	7pm-8pm Packed lunch £5.00
Distance from C2C	2 miles Pub 20 yds

3 Crowns Commended. *(See advertisement page 100.)*
"Come this way - start/finish in Whitley Bay. A quality cyclist-friendly historical family-run hotel. All rooms en-suite. Bar, restaurant, sauna."

Mrs D. A. Jack Lindsay Guest House, 50 Victoria Ave,
Whitley Bay, Tyne & Wear NE26 2BA

Telephone	**0191 252 7341**
Rooms	2 single + 3 double + 3 twin + 3 family
B&B	From £18.00 Packed lunch available
Distance from C2C	¾ mile Pub 50 yds

Registered 1997 Quality Award.

Tynemouth and Whitley Bay

Marlborough Hotel 20 - 21 East Parade, Central
Promenade, Whitley Bay NE26 1AP
Telephone **0191 251 3628** Fax 0191 252 5033
Rooms 15 double/single/twin *(most en-suite)*
B&B £20.00-£27.50
Evening meal £9.50 Packed lunch £3.00
Distance from C2C c. 4 miles from end of route
3 Crowns Commended. *"An attractive well-maintained hotel situated on the promenade. A good standard of accommodation in smart modern bedrooms (2 on the ground floor)."*

Tynemouth Station Tynemouth Station,
 Urban Bothy Station Terrace, Tynemouth NE30 4RE
Telephone **0191 258 3167**
Residential accommodation within the newly restored station building. *(See advertisement on page 104)*

Stamfordham

Mrs V. Fitzpatrick Church House, Stamfordham,
Northumberland NE18 0PB

Telephone	**01661 886736** Mobile 0589 312623
Rooms	2 twin
B&B	£20.00
Evening meal	No Packed lunch £3.00-£4.00
Distance from route	On route Pub nearby

"Pretty village green, old village pubs. 17th-c cream painted stone house of character on south side of green, private residence."

**Mr and Mrs
  D. Nicholson** The Bay Horse Inn, Southside,
Stamfordham, Newcastle-upon-Tyne
NE18 0OB

Telephone	**01661 886244** Fax 01661 881254
Rooms	1 single + 4 double + 1 family/twin
B&B	£25.00-£30.00
Evening meal	6.30-9.30pm Packed lunch £4.00
Distance from route	On route Pub

Commended. *"16th-c traditional country village Inn. Family-run. All rooms en-suite."*

Bellingham

**Mr and Mrs
  Forster** Crofters End, The Croft, Bellingham,
Hexham, Northumberland NE48 2JY

Telephone	**01434 220034**
Rooms	1 single + 1 double + 1 twin
B&B	£15.00
Evening meal	No
Packed lunch	£2.50 *(prior notice please)*
Distance from route	½ mile Pubs nearby

(No smoking please.) *"End terrace family home on outskirts of village. Also on Pennine Way. Homely ex-farming family."*

BELLINGHAM

This ancient little market town, known locally as "Bellin-jum", nestles at the foot of some of the wildest and most barren fells in Northumberland. There are medieval references to Bellingham Castle belonging to the King of Scotland's forester, but sadly no trace remains.

Bellingham Bridge

St Cuthbert's Church is unique with its stone roof and extremely narrow windows. Both features were some defence against the marauding Scots who twice burnt it to the ground. In its graveyard lies the famous "Long Pack" which is responsible for one of Northumbrian's most notorious tales of murder, intrigue and deception.

PLACES OF INTEREST
Hareshaw Linn   Superb waterfall, ° mile walk
St Cuthbert's Well   Reputed to be healing water

PLACES TO EAT
The Cheviot Hotel   Restaurant and bar meals
Fountain Tea Room   Good cheese scones!

BIKE REPAIRS
Village Country   Do hold some spare parts
Store   01434 220027

Bellingham

David and June Minchin   Westfield House, Bellingham, nr Hexham, Northumberland NE48 2DP

Telephone/Fax   **01434 220340**
Rooms   2 double + 2 twin *(all en-suite)*
B&B   £23.00-£27.00
Evening meal   £15.00   Packed lunch £4.50
Distance from route   On route   Pub nearby
(No smoking please.) **2 Crowns Highly Commended.**

Mrs L. M. Turner   The Black Bull Hotel, The Main, Bellingham, Hexham, NE48 2JP

Telephone   **01434 220226**
Rooms   1 double + 4 twin
B&B   £14.50-£15.00
Evening meal   Bar meals £4.25-£4.50
Packed lunch   £2.00-£3.00
Distance from route   On route   Hotel has public bar
(No smoking please.) *"Friendly, cosy and warm, in centre of town."*

Mrs Karren Waller   The Cheviot Hotel, Main Street, Bellingham, Northumberland NE48 2AN

Telephone/Fax   **01434 220696**
Rooms   1 single + 2 double + 3 twin
B&B   £22.50
Evening meal   £5.00-£15.00
Packed lunch   Available on request
Distance from route   On route   Hotel has public bar
(No smoking please.) **2 Crowns.**

Greenhaugh

Ian and Gloria Armstrong The Hollybush Inn, Greenhaugh, Tarset, Hexham, Northumberland NE48 1PW
Telephone **01434 240391**
Rooms 2 double + 1 twin *(2 en-suite)*
B&B £22.00-£24.00
Evening meal Available Packed lunch available
Distance from route 1 mile

1 Crown. *"200-year-old Inn retaining much of its original rustic character, with cosy log fires. Newly refurbished bedrooms, with tea/coffee-making facilities, radio alarm clocks and hairdryers."*

Stannersburn

Robin Kershaw The Pheasant Inn, Stannersburn, Kielder Water, Hexham, NE48 1DD
Telephone/Fax **01434 240382**
Rooms 4 double + 3 twin + 1 family
B&B £28.00
Evening meal £6.95, 3-course meal £12.00-£15.00
Packed lunch £5.00
Distance from route 1 mile Public bar

(No smoking in bedrooms and dining room please.) **3 Crowns Commended.** *"A traditional country Inn, bursting with character. Stone walls, beams and open fires provide its cosy atmosphere. Real ale, good home-cooking, all rooms en-suite."*

FALSTONE

This secluded little hamlet lost nearly 80% of its parish under the waters of Kielder Reservoir. Today the village is a tranquil beauty spot surrounded by trees, and a good stopping place for the cyclist with post office, shop and pub. A tributary to the Tyne bubbles its way through the centre of the village and, depending on the time of year, it is possible to see dippers, heron, cormorants, goosanders, and with luck you may witness the miraculous sight of salmon spawning.

The Village Hall   Teas. Floor-sleeping space, cooking and washing facilities
Hylton Pyner 01434 240296

Post Office   Mrs Entwistle

The Blackcock   Old world pub with good food

Falstone

Maureen and Ken Entwistle Braefoot, Falstone, Hexham, Northumberland NE48 1AA
Telephone **01434 240238**
Rooms 2 single + 1 double
B&B £15.00 Packed lunch £2.50 - £3.00
Distance from route On route Pubs nearby
(No smoking please.) *"Old stone house, private lounge, in beautiful location in village centre, 2 pubs, easy access."*

Mr Hylton Pyner Falstone Village Hall, Falstone, Hexham, Northumberland NE48 1AA
Telephone **01434 240296**
Floor space available for groups of up to 25 people. Showers, toilets, washing and cooking facilities. Bring your own sleeping bag and roll mat. Price £3.00 per person. Groups over 20 at £2.00 per person.

Tom and Alex Richards The Blackcock Inn, Falstone, Hexham, Northumberland NE48 1AA
Telephone **01434 240200** Fax 01434 240036
Rooms 4 single + 2 double + 2 twin
B&B £20.00-£28.00
Evening meal £3.00-£10.00 Packed lunch £3.25
Distance from route On route Public bar
(No smoking in bedrooms please.) **3 Crowns Commended.**
"Lovely old black-leaded range in bar, real ale, gourmet restaurant or bar meals."

Falstone

Myra Grimwood Woodside, Low Yarrow, Falstone,
Hexham, Northumberland NE48 1BG
Telephone **01434 240443**
Rooms 1 double + 2 twin
B&B £16.60
Evening meal From £8.00 *(prior notice please)*
Packed lunch £2.50-£3.00
Distance from route On route Pub nearby
(No smoking please.) **Listed Commended.** *"Picturesque hamlet near Kielder Water. Lovely views over secluded valley, good home-cooking."*

John and Shirley Richardson High Yarrow Farm, Falstone, Hexham
Northumberland NE48 1BG
Telephone **01434 240264**
Rooms 1 twin + 1 single *(no smoking please)*
B&B £15.00 Packed lunch £3.00
Distance from route ½ mile Pubs nearby
"150-year-old farmhouse on working farm situated at the head of Kielder Water."

Mrs Karen Hodgson Ridge End Farm, Falstone,
nr Kielder Water, Hexham, NE48 1DE
Telephone **01434 240395**
Rooms 1 twin + 1 family *(both en-suite)*
B&B £18.00-£25.00 *(no smoking please)*
Evening meal No Packed lunch £3.00
Distance from route ½ mile Pub nearby
Two Crowns Commended. *"This is a 16th-c bastle house (a fortified farmhouse), the historic home of border reivers with 5ft thick walls, private lounge, log fires. Cottage available."* **(See advertisement on page 144.)**

KIELDER WATER

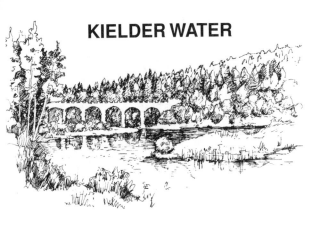

A wild and romantic place, Kielder Water is the heart of Border Reiver country. It is hard to imagine the cattle rustling, kidnapping and arson that flourished here in the 15th and 16th centuries. Today Kielder's stunning scenery, peace and quiet welcome all visitors. There are a wealth of facilities for the cyclist here. Northumbria Water, who created the resevoir, have been responsible for a good deal of the inspiration behind the Reivers Cycle Route.

PLACES OF INTEREST
Tower Knowe Visitor Centre
An Information Centre with extensive gift shop and audio visual exhibition.

Leaplish Waterside Park
Heated swimming pool and sauna, campsite, licensed restaurant, sculpture trail, bird of prey centre, and much more.

KIELDER VILLAGE

Situated at the head of the reservoir, Kielder, once in a wild and uncultivated country surrounded by moors and bogs, is now a purpose-built forestry village cocooned by pine trees Before the turn of the century Kielder Castle which stands guard over the village would have been hidden and alone at the valley head. It was buit in 1775 by the Duke of Northumberland as his hunting lodge. Shooting parties travelled from London on the sleeper and were met at the station by pony and trap. To carry home a bag of 200 brace of grouse and blackcock in a day was not unusual. Kielder is an oasis for the cyclist with shop, pub and post office.

PLACES OF INTEREST
Kielder Castle Forest   Shop, tea room, WCs
  Park Information Centre 01434 250209

PLACES TO EAT
The Anglers Arms   01434 250234

BIKE SHOPS
Kielder Bikes   Ken and Kim Bone, opposite the
                            Castle 01434 250392

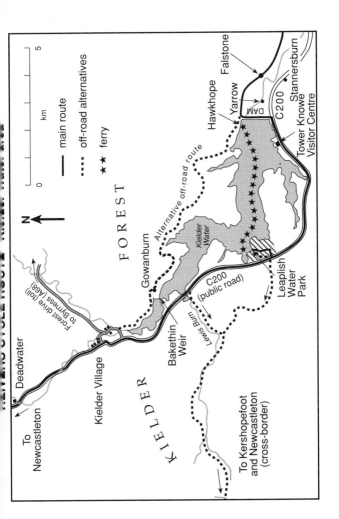

Kielder

Mrs Janet Scott   Gowan Burn, Kielder, Hexham,
Northumberland NE48 1HL

Telephone	**01434 250254**
Rooms	1 double + 1 twin + 1 family
B&B	£16.00
Evening meal	Light meal Packed lunch £2.50
Distance from route	On route Pub 1½ miles

Listed. *"Superb views, peaceful old farmhouse on edge of Kielder Water."*

Mrs Fiona Hall   Deadwater Farm, Kielder, Hexham,
Northumberland NE48 1EW

Telephone	**01434 250216**
Rooms	1 double + 1 twin + 1 family
B&B	£15.00
Evening meal	Snack £4.00 Packed lunch £3.00
Distance from route	100 yds Pub nearby

(No smoking except in lounge please.) **Listed.** *"Old stone-built farmhouse in peaceful surroundings on Scotland/England border."*

NEWCASTLETON

Newcastleton, with its broad Georgian streets and open squares, was purpose designed and built from scratch by the Duke of Buccleugh in 1792. Due to the changes in agriculture there was a need for more village-based employment such as handloom weaving. They were built with large windows to let in light for the new cottage industries.

The town has a post office, several pubs, a wonderfully eccentric combined tea and antique shop and several guesthouses. If your time and energy allow don't miss a short detour to Hermitage Castle. This mysterious and magic place not only witnessed long years of turbulent border reiving, but

it played host to the tragic Mary Queen of Scots when she snatched two hours' rendezvous with her lover Boswell.

Hermitage Castle

Newcastleton

Hazel White 12 Whitchester Lane, Newcastleton,
Roxburghshire, TD9 0RD
Telephone **013873 75826**
Rooms 1 twin
B&B £14.00 (£15.50 single)
Evening meal No Packed lunch £2.50
Distance from route On route Pub nearby
(No smoking except in lounge please.) "Small cosy terraced
cottage, off the main road. Secure environment."

Mrs Pamela Bailey Mill Accommodation &
Copeland Trekking, Bailey, Newcastleton,
Roxburghshire TD9 0TR
Telephone/Fax **016977 48617**
Rooms 2 single + 4 double + 4 twin + 2 family
B&B £15.00-£20.00
Evening meal £2.50-£8.00 Packed lunch £2.00
Distance from route On route Pub on site
3 Key Commended. *"Courtyard apartments for self-catering
or B&B. Relax in our Jacuzzi, sauna or solarium, then have a
drink and meal (delivered to your apartment) or in our licensed
bar."*

Elaine and Woodside, North Hermitage Street,
Campbell Newcastleton,Roxburghshire TD9 0RZ
Adamson Telephone **013873 75431**
Rooms 2 double + 2 twin + 1 single
B&B £15.00
Evening meal £8.00 Packed lunch £3.00
Distance from route On route Pub nearby
(Mainly a non-smoking house.) "North end of village set in its
own grounds. Spacious residents lounge."

Newcastleton

Mrs Linda Stenhouse

Borders Honey Farm, Newcastleton,
Roxburghshire TD9 0SG

Telephone/Fax	**013873 76737**
Rooms	1 double + 1 twin
B&B	£20.00-£23.00
Evening meal	£8.00-£15.00 Packed lunch £3.00
Distance from route	On route Pub nearby

(No smoking please.) **2 Crowns Commended.** *"A warm welcome awaits you in our peaceful Borders farmhouse set amidst beautiful forested countryside. Excellent cycling area. Good home-cooking."*

Bewcastle

Fiona, Maggie and Dave

Lime Kiln Inn, Bewcastle,
Telephone **016977 48229**
Meals only, no accommodation

Kirkcambeck

Marjorie Stobart

Cracrop Farm, Kirkcambeck,
nr Brampton, Cumbria CA8 2BW

Telephone	**016977 48245** Fax 016977 48333
Rooms	1 single + 2 double + 1 twin *(all en-suite)*
B&B	£25.00-£30.00
Evening meal	£8.00-£15.00 *(prior notice please)*
Packed lunch	£4.00 *(prior notice please)*
Distance from route	1½ miles Pub 3 miles

Highly Commended. *"A warm welcome to our comfortable farmhouse. Luxuriously-appointed spacious bedrooms, TV and drinks tray, relax in the sauna (small extra charge) or spa bath. Superb traditional English breakfast."*

BEWCASTLE

The famous Bewcastle Cross has survived 1300 years of relentless border weather in St Cuthbert's church yard. The church and remains of the castle stand remote and almost alone save for a farmhouse in this forgotten outpost in a great sweep of wild and rugged countryside. There is a display of interpretative panels nearby in a small Heritage Centre. They tell the story of the Anglo-Saxon cross. The runic insriptions and carving are of a very high quality for this period in history.

Summer is for grazing, but autumn is for raiding

Just like football, our raiding friends were far too busy tending crops and fattening the cattle in summer to be doing any reiving, but as soon as the crops were gathered and the horses fit they would be hot foot across whichever border to get down to the serious winter business of stealing each other,s wives, girl-friends, cattle, sheep and carefully-stored winter goods again.

Walton

Mrs Una Armstrong	Town Head Farm, Walton, nr Brampton, Cumbria CA8 2DJ
Telephone	**016977 2730**
Rooms	1 double + 1 family
B&B	£15.00
Evening meal	6pm-6.30pm Packed lunch £3.00
Distance from route	400 yds Pub 400 yds

(No smoking in bedrooms please.) **Commended.** *"Cosy farmhouse with friendly atmosphere on working mixed farm. Overlooks village green with play area. Picturesque views of Pennines and Lakeland hills. Hadrian's Wall nearby."*

Askerton Castle

Catlowdy near Longtown

Jack and Margaret Sisson
Bessietown Farm Country Guesthouse
Catlowdy, Longtown, Carlisle CA6 5QP

Telephone/Fax	**01228 577219 + 577019**
Rooms	2 single + 4 double + 4 twin + 2 family
B&B	£22.50-£23.50 *(no smoking please)*
Evening meal	£11.00
Distance from route	1½ miles Pub 6 miles

3 Crowns Highly Commended, AA QQQQQ. *"Warm welcome and delicious food. Drinks licence. All rooms en-suite. Indoor heated swimming pool open May to mid-September."*

Jane Lawson
Craigburn Farm, Catlowdy,
nr Longtown, Carlisle CA6 5QP

Telephone/Fax	01228 577214 + 577014
Rooms	2 double + 3 twin + 1 family *(all en-suite)*
B&B	£21.00 *(no smoking in bedrooms please)*
Evening meal	£12.00 Packed lunch £3.50
Distance from route	2 miles Pub 3 miles

3 Crowns Commended. *"Friendly relaxed atmosphere. Some four-poster beds. Tea/coffee and TV. Delicious home-cooking, desserts a speciality. Licensed. Credit cards accepted."*

Ruth Casson
Liddel Lodge, Catlowdy, Penton,
nr Carlisle, Cumbria CA6 5QN

Telephone	**01228 577335**
Rooms	1 single + 1 double + 1 family
B&B	£17.00-£18.00 *(no smoking please)*
Evening meal	£10.00 Packed lunch £5.00
Distance from route	1½ miles Pub 1½ miles

2 Crowns commended. *"Hunting lodge with panoramic views of Liddesdale. Excellent base for exploring the Borders. Home produce and cooking. Brochure available."*

CARLISLE

This great border city greets its guests with open arms, but not so many years ago any visitor would have been treated with suspicion. It was the nerve-centre for bitter feuds and bloody battles created by the long-running dispute over the border betwen England and Scotland. Early in its history it was an important Roman headquarters for Hadrian's Wall. In 1092 William the Conqueror's son started to build the castle where later the unfortunate Mary Queen of Scots was incarcerated.

PLACES OF INTEREST

Tullie House Museum and Art Gallery	Excellent audio-visual interpretation of the Border Reivers
Carlisle Castle	Medieval dungeons, exhibitions
Carlisle Cathedral	Founded in 1122, fine wood carving and wall panels

PLACES TO EAT

The GrapeVine	Excellent, value for money, vegetarian food 01228 546617
Pierre Victoire	French cuisine 01228 515111

BIKE REPAIRS

Palace Cycle	122 Botchergate 01228 523142
Scotby Cycles	Bridge St 01228 546931

Carlisle

G. C. Webster Angus Hotel, 14 Scotland Road,
Carlisle CA3 9DG

Telephone **01228 523546** Fax 01228 531895
Rooms 3 single + 3 double + 8 family/twin
B&B £17.00-£42.00
Evening meal £6.00-£15.00
Packed lunch £3.00-£5.00
Distance from route On route *(See advert page 145)*
(Mainy a non-smoking hotel.) **AA QQQQ Selected.** *"Cosy Victorian town house offering personal hospitality, superb food in Almonds Bistro, local cheeses, home-baked bread and draught beer. Secure car parking and cycle storage."*

Eric and Daphne Houghton Corner House, 87 Petteril Street,
Carlisle, Cumbria CA1 2AW

Telephone/Fax **01228 541942**
Rooms 4 double + 3 twin + 2 family
B&B £15.00-£18.00
Evening meal £5.00-£8.50 Packed lunch £3.50
Distance from route On route Pub nearby
AA QQQ. *"Comfortable rooms, newly refurbished, en-suite with all facilities including hairdryers and satellite TV. Good English breakfast, easy walking distance of city centre."*

Jeremy Dickenson Crown and Mitre Hotel, English Street,
Carlisle, Cumbria CA3 8HZ

Telephone **01228 525491** Fax 01228 514553
Rooms 97 B&B £44.00-£77.00
Meals £3.50-£20.00 Packed lunch £4.00
Distance from route On route Hotel has Public Bar
RAC***, AA***. *"Grand Edwardian Hotel, Grade II Listed building, full of character and comfort. Executive rooms available Swimming pool, Jacuzzi."*

THE EASTERN FELLS OF THE LAKE DISTRICT NATIONAL PARK

Tread softly as you pass through this miraculously untouched corner of England!

St Mungo hurried here in the 6th century for he had heard muffled whispers that word of the Gospels had not reached the ears of the wild and unruly people living in the Eastern Fells! Many of the local churches are named after his other more formal name, St Kentigern.

HESKET NEWMARKET

Ask a local inhabitant the name of an ash tree and he will tell you it is a 'Hesh'. Hesket means the place of the ash trees. Local farmers bought and sold bulls at the market cross. A generous village green invites travellers to taste the local brewed beer and rest awhile. There is a well stocked village shop, a post office, pub and several guest-houses. The Crown Inn is famous for its own home-brewed ales. They are named after local fells: Blencathra, Great Cock-up, and Doris in honour of the landlord's mother on her 90th birthday.

Hesket-New-Market

Mrs Dorothy Studholme

Newlands Grange, Hesket-New-Market, Wigton, Cumbria CA7 8HP

Telephone	**016974 78676**
Rooms	1 single + 2 double + 2 twin/family
B&B	£16.00-£19.00
Evening meal	£6.50 Packed lunch £3.00
Distance from route	On route Pub 1½ miles

"Newlands Grange is a working farm looking onto the Caldbeck Fells, house featuring old oak beams and open fire. Good home-cooking and a warm welcome awaits all."

Margaret Monkhouse

Denton House, Hesket-New-Market, Caldbeck, Cumbria CA7 8JG

Telephone	**016974 78415**
Rooms	1 single + 2 double + 1 twin + 3 family
B&B	£18.50-£20.00
Evening meal	£8.50-£10.00 Packed lunch £3.00
Distance from route	On route
Pub	Nearby *(with own brewery)*

(No smoking in bedrooms please.) "Warm family atmosphere welcomes everyone, with log fires and home-cooking. Most rooms are en-suite."

CALDBECK

Named after the river (Cold-beck), Caldbeck was a thriving rural industrial centre before steam-power and the Industrial Revolution. There is still a clog-maker in the village centre. In 1800 there were no fewer than 8 water-powered mills making bobbins, woollens and grinding corn.

__The Priests Mill__ which has been beautifully restored houses a craft centre, display area and restaurant with a picture gallery.

In the churchyard is John Peel's grave and that of Mary, the Beauty of Buttermere who was the subject of the novel 'The Maid of Buttermere' by Melvyn Bragg.

PLACES OF INTEREST

The Howk	A hidden gem upstream from the village
The Clog Maker	Will Strong: next to the bridge

PLACES TO EAT

Priests Mill	Delicious vegetarian food: you'll return!
Odd Fellows Arms	Wholesome country food

After Caldbeck the route winds its way round the fell: an area known locally as Back 'a Skiddaw. __Parkend Restaurant__ and __The Snooty Fox__ are the only watering holes for several miles.

Caldbeck

Mrs Nan Savage   Swaledale Watch, Whelpo, nr Caldbeck, Wigton, Cumbria CA7 8HQ
Telephone   **016974 78409**
Rooms   2 double + 1 twin + 2 family
B&B   £17.00-£21.00
Evening meal   £10.50-£11.00 *(prior notice please)*
Packed lunch   £3.50 approx *(prior notice please)*
Distance from route   On route   Pub 1 mile
(No smoking please.) **2 Crowns Highly Commended, AA Selected QQQQ.** *"Enjoy great comfort in beautiful surroundings on our working farm. A warm welcome, hot bath and good food awaits you. First there gets the Jacuzzi!"*

Cumbria Outdoors   Fellside, nr Caldbeck, Wigton,
  Fellside Centre   Cumbria CA7 8HA
Telephone   **017687 72816** Fax 017687 75108
Rooms   Dormitory accommodation for 38
B&B   £6.50-£22.50
Evening meal   From £3.88
Distance from C2C   On route   Pub 2 miles
(No smoking please.)

Mrs C. Cornes   Parkend Restaurant & Country Hotel, nr Caldbeck, Wigton   CA7 8HH
Telephone   **016974 78494**
Rooms   4 double + 1 twin + 1 family
B&B   £24.00-£32.00
Evening meal   5.30pm-9pm   Packed lunch £4.00
Distance from route   ¼ mile   Licenced bar
(No smoking in dining room please.) **3 Crown Commended.** *"17th-c converted farmhouse 1½ miles from Caldbeck village. Comfortable en-suite rooms and fine food."*

Uldale

Mr and Mrs Geoff Harmer	The Snooty Fox, Uldale, nr Carlisle, Cumbria CA5 1HA
Telephone	**016973 71479** Fax 016973 71910
Minicom	016973 71316
Rooms	2 double + 2 family
B&B	£19.00
Evening meal	£4.00-£10.00
Packed lunch	£5.00 Pub on premises

(No smoking in bedrooms please.) "Family-run pub restaurant, lounge, bar, games room. Good food, relaxing atmosphere."

Ireby

Robin and Annie Binny	Ellenside, Ireby, nr Carlisle, Cumbria CA5 1EH
Telephone	**016973 71256** Mobile 0411 721018
Rooms	1 double + 2 twin *(all en-suite)*
B&B	£20.00-£25.00
Packed lunch	£3.50 Pub nearby
Distance from route	1½ miles

"Charming Regency house built in 1820, facing south with verandah overlooking garden and tennis court. Magnificent views of the Lake District, fells and mountains."

For tourist information and accommodation in Cockermouth please turn to pages 21 - 23

Youth Hostels

YHA, Northern Region, PO Box 11, Matlock, Derbyshire
DE4 2XA (inc SAE) *(See advertisement page 103.)*
Tel **01629 825850**

Newcastle-upon-Tyne Youth Hostel
107 Jesmond Road, Newcastle-upon-Tyne, NE2 1NJ
£5.15 (under 18s), £7.70 (adults) + Breakfast £2.85
Tel **0191 281 2570**

Once Brewed Youth Hostel
Military Road, Bardon Mill, Hexham, Northumberland
NE47 7AN £5.70 (under 18s), £8.50 (adults)
Tel **01434 344360**

Bellingham Youth Hostel
Woodburn Road, Bellingham, Hexham, Northumberland
NE48 2ED £4.25 (under 18s), £6.25 (adults)
Tel **01434 220313**

Carlisle Campus (University of Northumbria)
Old Brewery Residences, Bridge Lane, Caldewgate, Carlisle
CA2 5SW (available July 15-September 13)
Tel **01228 597352**

Carrock Fell Youth Hostel
High Row Cottage, Haltcliffe, Hesket Newmarket, Wigton,
Cumbria CA7 8JT £4.75 (under 18s), £6.95 (adults)
Tel **016974 78325**

Cockermouth Youth Hostel
Double Mills, Cockermouth, Cumbria CA13 0DS
£4.75 (under 18s), £6.95 (adults)
Tel **01900 822561**

Camping and Caravans Sites

BELLINGHAM
Brown Rigg   01434 220175
The Main Farm   01434 220258

FALSTONE
The Village Hall   01434 240296

KIELDER
Leaplish   01434 250278
Kielder Village   01434 250291

NEWCASTLETON
The Lidalia Caravan/Camp   01387 375203

LONGTOWN
Oakbank Lakes Country Park   01228 791108
High Gaitle   01228 791819

CARLISLE
Orton Grange   01228 710252
has a swimming pool!

DALSTON
Dalston Hall   01228 710165

CALDBECK
Friars Hall   016974 78633

BEWALDETH
North Lakes   017687 76510

COCKERMOUTH
Violet Bank   01900 822169

Useful Telephone Numbers

Weather News

North East England Weathercall	0891 500 418
Cumbria & the Lake District Weathercall	0891 500 419

Tourist Information Centres

Gateshead	0191 477 3478
Newcastle upon Tyne	0191 261 0610
Whitley Bay	0191 200 8535
Hawick	01450 372547
Bellingham	01434 220616
Kielder	01434 240398
Longtown	01228 792835
Carlisle	01228 625600
Cockermouth	01900 822634
Silloth-on-Solway	01697 331944
Whitehaven	01946 695678
Maryport	01900 813738

Travel Information: Bus, Coach and Train

Northumberland County Council	01670 533128
Tyne & Wear County Council Travellink	0191 232 5325
Stagecoach Cumberland	01946 63222
National Express	0990 808080
National Express Newcastle	0191 232 3300
National Rail Enquiries Line	0345 484 950
Scotrail Enquiries Line	0345 550033
Cycle Booking Line NW Trains	0161 228 5906

Bike Shops and Repairs

Metro Centre   The Bike Place, 8 Allison Court   0191 488 3137

Newcastle   Newcastle Cycle Centre, 165 Westgate Rd
               0191 230 3022
               Dentons, Blenheim St 0191 232 3903

Byker   Hardisty Cycles, 5 Union Rd   0191 265 8619

Bellingham   Village and Country Store do some spare
               parts 01434 220027

Kielder   Kielder Castle, Ken and Kim Bone
               01434 250392 **(see page 144)**

Carlisle   Mike Lee, Palace Cycle Stores, 122 Botchergate
               01228 523142**(See advertisement page 146.)**
               Scotby Cycles, Bridge Street
               01228 546931

Cockermouth   Derwent Cycles 01900 822113
               The Wordsworth Hotel Bike Hire 01900 822757

"Take nothing but photographs
Leave nothing but tyre-tracks"

Near Ennerdale

How to get home

There are various options for leaving
Newcastle or Sunderland:

* Mainline Intercity trains from Newcastle

* Local train to Newcastle (only 2 bikes per train)
  to connect with Intercity East Coast

* Continue to cycle up coast from Seaburn to
  South Shields, and thence to Gateshead or
  Newcastle (via Ferry or Cycle Tunnel)

* Liaise and book with one of the taxi or tour
  companies advertised in this book, to get you
  back to the start in Cumbria

  Holiday Lakeland   *016973 71871*
  Stanley Taxis   *01207 237424*
  Ted Gilman   *0191 284 7534*

* Book into a local B&B and have a celebratory
  party!

* Cycle back on the the Reivers Cycle Route